A Brief
Introduction to
CLASSICAL
MECHANICS
with Illustrative
Problems

A Brief Introduction to CLASSICAL MECHANICS with Illustrative Problems

Shahen Hacyan

Instituto de Física, Universidad Nacional Autónoma de México, Mexico

World Scientific

NEW JERSEY · LONDON · SINGAPORE · BEIJING · SHANGHAI · HONG KONG · TAIPEI · CHENNAI · TOKYO

Published by

World Scientific Publishing Co. Pte. Ltd.

5 Toh Tuck Link, Singapore 596224

USA office: 27 Warren Street, Suite 401-402, Hackensack, NJ 07601

UK office: 57 Shelton Street, Covent Garden, London WC2H 9HE

Library of Congress Control Number: 2023944495

British Library Cataloguing-in-Publication Data
A catalogue record for this book is available from the British Library.

A BRIEF INTRODUCTION TO CLASSICAL MECHANICS WITH ILLUSTRATIVE PROBLEMS

ISBN 978-981-127-472-5 (hardcover)
ISBN 978-981-127-535-7 (paperback)
ISBN 978-981-127-473-2 (ebook for institutions)
ISBN 978-981-127-474-9 (ebook for individuals)

For any available supplementary material, please visit
https://www.worldscientific.com/worldscibooks/10.1142/13365#t=suppl

Desk Editor: Nur Syarfeena Binte Mohd Fauzi

Typeset by Stallion Press
Email: enquiries@stallionpress.com

Printed in Singapore

PER BEATRICE

Preface

This textbook is based on my lecture notes for a course on Classical Mechanics that I have offered for several years to graduate students in Physics at the Faculty of Science of the Autonomous National University of Mexico (*Universidad Nacional Autónoma de México*, UNAM). The course is aimed at students with a basic knowledge of calculus, and is designed to be covered during one or two full semesters, depending on its intensity.

Since there are many excellent textbooks on Classical Mechanics at various levels, the reader may wonder if another text could be of any use. This textbook is restricted to the most basic elements of the subject, and the details of the calculations are presented a step-by-step derivation of the fundamental formulas. The purpose is to give an overview of the subject with various illustrative examples and to show how to apply the general results to relevant problems in Classical Mechanics. My own experience (which may be old fashioned but efficient!) is that the best way for a student to learn the techniques of calculation and grasp the basic concepts of the matter under study is by watching his/her teacher developing such step-by-step derivations "by hand" on the blackboard (or any equivalent device) and by carefully following the deductions of each step, being even watchful of possible slips by the teacher and warning him/her immediately. It is contrary to all pedagogical methods to simply show formulas on a screen (in PowerPoint, for instance) with only a brief comment on their meaning.

It is for this reason that there are no exercises in this textbook, since it is precisely about acquiring the skill to solve exercises. Accordingly, the reader is strongly recommended to follow each deduction in the book, to carefully check all the formulas, and finally measure his/her skills with the many exercises that can be found in standard classical textbooks. The reader may also note that some topics are treated in full detail, while others are only sketched; the purpose is to familiarize students with the handling of the most basic topics. Thus, for instance, I have tried to work out in detail some selected problems and give a general idea of the topics treated in the last chapters. As for the figures, I have chosen to present most of them as I usually draw on the blackboard in front of my students.

Shahen Hacyan
Mexico City, May 2023

Contents

Chapter 1

Force and Energy

Isaac Newton (1642–1727) defined his famous three laws of motion in the *Principia*[1] in the following form:

Law I: Every body persists in its state of being at rest or of moving uniformly straight forward, except insofar as it is compelled to change its state by force impressed.

Law II: The alteration of motion is ever proportional to the motive force impressed; and is made in the direction of the right line in which that force is impressed.

Law III: To every action there is always opposed an equal reaction: or the mutual actions of two bodies upon each other are always equal, and directed to contrary parts.

These can be summarized in modern terms as follows:

(1) In the absence of forces, a body moves in a straight line, without altering its velocity. (Of course, we must assume that we know what a straight line is, and that the space is Euclidian.)

(2) Force is the change of the quantity of motion defined as the product of mass and velocity.[2] Newton's second law relates the force $\mathbf{F}$ exerted on a particle of mass m to the change of the *quantity of motion*, or what we usually call the *momentum*,

---

[1] *Mathematical Principles of Natural Philosophy*. English translation from the original Latin by Andrew Motte, revised by Florian Cajori.

[2] Newton defined mass as the product of volume and density, but he never defined density. It seems that in his time, density was considered a more fundamental concept than mass.

defined as $m\mathbf{v}$, where $\mathbf{v}$ is the velocity of the particle. For constant mass, the second law can be written as

$$\mathbf{F} = m\ddot{\mathbf{r}}, \tag{1.1}$$

where $\mathbf{r}$ is the position vector of the particle under consideration and the dots represent derivatives with respect to time.

(3) To every action, there is a reaction of equal magnitude and opposite direction. For instance, the Earth attracts the Moon, and the Moon attracts the Earth with the same force; the accelerations of the two bodies are different because they have different masses. A falling stone also attracts the Earth, but due to the enormous mass difference, the acceleration of the Earth is imperceptible.

There has been much discussion on whether the second law is really a law or just the definition of force. Force is defined as that which changes a uniform motion, but what can be measured directly is the acceleration. In any case, the second law is a convenient definition of force in practical terms. It must be interpreted as the fact that the *particular* motion of a body depends on its initial position and velocity, but its acceleration (second derivative of the position) has a completely *general* character, which is independent of initial conditions. It is this general character of motion that permits to define force as a universal concept, independent of the initial values of the position and its first derivative.

1.1. Potential energy

Force is defined as a vector. A particularly important case is that of a force that can be obtained as the gradient of a scalar potential $U(\mathbf{r})$ that depends on the spatial coordinates only, that is,

$$\mathbf{F} = -\nabla U(\mathbf{r}). \tag{1.2}$$

In this case, Eq. (1.1) implies

$$-\dot{\mathbf{r}} \cdot \nabla U(\mathbf{r}) = m\dot{\mathbf{r}} \cdot \ddot{\mathbf{r}},$$

and, since $\dot{\mathbf{r}} \cdot \nabla = d/dt$, it follows that

$$\frac{d}{dt}\left(\frac{1}{2}m|\dot{\mathbf{r}}|^2 + U(\mathbf{r})\right) = 0.$$

We then obtain the important condition that the energy defined as

$$E = \frac{1}{2}m|\dot{\mathbf{r}}|^2 + U(\mathbf{r}), \qquad (1.3)$$

is a conserved quantity at all times consisting of two parts: the kinetic energy

$$\frac{1}{2}m|\dot{\mathbf{r}}|^2$$

and the potential energy $U(\mathbf{r})$.

Accordingly, the total energy E can be determined from the initial conditions. For instance, if the motion of the particle starts from rest, $\mathbf{v} = \mathbf{0}$, at a certain time at the position $\mathbf{r} = \mathbf{r_0}$, then

$$E = U(\mathbf{r_0}).$$

The definition (1.3) of the (constant) energy is very convenient, since it is enough to take its first time derivative to obtain the equations of motion, as we will see in all of the following. Forces satisfying the condition (1.2) are called conservative.

1.2. One-dimensional problems

Consider the motion of a particle in one dimension, with coordinate, say x. In this case, since $v = \dot{x}$, Eq. (1.3) implies

$$t = \int \frac{\sqrt{m}\,dx}{\sqrt{2(E - U(x))}}, \qquad (1.4)$$

as the relation between time and position, $t(x)$, for a given value of the energy; the limits of integration can be determined by the initial conditions. Thus, given any potential, a one-dimensional problem of motion can always be solved by quadratures (i.e., a one-dimensional integral). Clearly, $E - U(x)$ must always be positive, but for a negative $U(x)$, the energy E can be both positive or negative (this is the case of gravitational force, as we will see in Chapter 2).

1.2.1. *Constant force*

The simplest non-trivial case is the motion under a constant force, for instance, the vertical fall of a body with a constant acceleration g. The energy is simply

$$E = \frac{1}{2}mv^2 + mgx, \tag{1.5}$$

where $v = \dot{x}$ is the velocity. A first derivative yields

$$\ddot{x} + g = 0,$$

meaning that the acceleration is constant, as already known.

It is instructive to consider the energy equation (1.5) as describing a curve in the (x, v) plane, which is called the *phase space*.[3] The trajectories are parabolas depending on the values of the energy, as seen in Fig. 1.1. The interpretation of this figure should be clear: for instance, a particle dropped from a height $x_0 = h$ with zero initial velocity $v(h) = 0$ has energy $E = mgh$ and reaches the ground $x = 0$ with velocity $v(0) = \sqrt{2gh}$. Note that if the potential energy increases with height x, then the velocity of fall is negative.

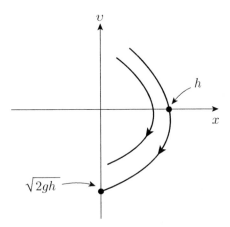

Fig. 1.1. Trajectory in (x, v) space of a uniformly accelerated particle.

---

[3] Actually, the phase space is defined in terms of the position and the momentum, but we take the mass as constant and consider the velocity in our simple examples.

1.2.2. *Harmonic oscillator*

An important example is the *harmonic oscillator* that describes the motion of a particle subject to a linear force, such as a massive bob tied to a spring with the Hooke constant k. The equation of motion is

$$m\ddot{x} = -kx,$$

and the associated potential is

$$U(x) = \frac{1}{2}kx^2.$$

It is convenient to define $\omega = \sqrt{k/m}$ as the characteristic angular frequency of the oscillator (with units T^{-1}) and write the above equation of motion in the basic form

$$\ddot{x} + \omega^2 x = 0, \tag{1.6}$$

independently of the mass m. The general solution is

$$x(t) = x_0 \cos(\omega t) + \omega^{-1}\dot{x}_0 \sin(\omega t),$$
$$\dot{x}(t) = -\omega x_0 \sin(\omega t) + \dot{x}_0 \cos(\omega t), \tag{1.7}$$

where x_0 and $\dot{x}_0$ are the initial position and velocity, respectively. From these formulas, ω can be identified as the angular frequency of oscillation, and thus the period of oscillation is

$$P = 2\pi/\omega.$$

Note that this period is entirely independent of the amplitude (and thus of the initial position): it only depends on the Hooke constant of the spring and the mass of the attached bob.

The trajectories in phase space are now ellipses

$$\dot{x}^2 + \omega^2 x^2 = \frac{2E}{m}, \tag{1.8}$$

with axis $\sqrt{2E/m\omega^2}$ and $\sqrt{2E/m}$, as shown in Fig. 1.2. Of course, the energy E is a constant.

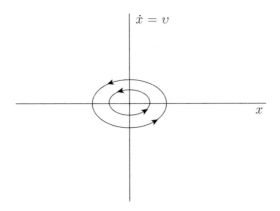

Fig. 1.2. Trajectory in (x, v) space of a harmonic oscillator.

One can also invert equations in (1.7),

$$x_0 = x(t) \cos(\omega t) - \omega^{-1} \dot{x}(t) \sin(\omega t),$$
$$\dot{x}_0 = \omega x(t) \sin(\omega t) + \dot{x}(t) \cos(\omega t),$$

(1.9)

and thus obtain two additional constants of motion that do depend explicitly on time.

The position at rest, $x = 0$, $\dot{x} = 0$ (and thus $E = 0$), is a particular solution which is stable, in the sense that any small perturbation of the initial position or velocity produces only a small deviation from that initial position. The perturbed trajectories are small ellipses in phase space centered around the point $x = 0$, $\dot{x} = 0$.

Another important case is that of the *inverted oscillator* for which

$$U(x) = -\frac{1}{2} k x^2,$$

with a negative sign. The corresponding solutions of the equation of motion are

$$x(t) = x_0 \cosh(\omega t) + \omega^{-1} \dot{x}_0 \sinh(\omega t),$$
$$\dot{x}(t) = \omega x_0 \sinh(\omega t) + \dot{x}_0 \cosh(\omega t).$$

(1.10)

The trajectories are hyperbolas in phase space,

$$\dot{x}^2 - \omega^2 x^2 = \frac{2E}{m},$$

as shown in Fig. 1.3.

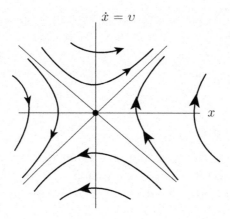

Fig. 1.3. Trajectory in (x, v) space of an inverted oscillator.

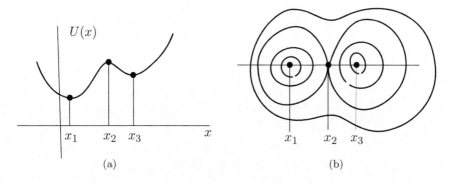

(a)   (b)

Fig. 1.4. (a) One-dimensional potential function. (b) Possible trajectories in (x, v) space of a particle in this potential.

Note now that in this case $x = 0$, $\dot{x} = 0$ is still a particular solution, but it is not stable: any small perturbation of the initial position or velocity produces an ever increasing deviation from the initial position (think of a marble standing on the tip of a needle).

1.2.3. *General case*

A more general situation is illustrated in Fig. 1.4(a), where a particular potential is shown with two minima: $E_1 = U(x_1)$ and

$E_2 = U(x_2)$, and one maximum at $E_3 = U(x_3)$. Possible trajectories are depicted in Fig. 1.4(b). Note that x_1 and x_2 are stable positions at rest, while x_3 is an unstable position. This qualitative form of trajectories in phase space is typical of stable and unstable trajectories.

1.2.4. *The pendulum*

Consider a pendulum consisting of a point-mass m hanging from a rigid rod of length l and negligible mass.

If the motion is restricted to a plane, as shown in Fig. 1.5, the energy is

$$E = \frac{1}{2}mv^2 + mgl(1 - \cos\theta), \tag{1.11}$$

with $v = l\dot{\theta}$. Taking the time derivative of the energy, the equation of motion follows as

$$\frac{d^2\theta}{dt^2} + \frac{g}{l}\sin\theta = 0, \tag{1.12}$$

and, according to Eq. (1.4), its solution is given by the integral

$$t = l \int \frac{\sqrt{m}\,d\theta}{\sqrt{2[E - mgl(1 - \cos\theta)]}}, \tag{1.13}$$

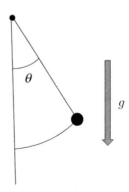

Fig. 1.5.   The simple plane pendulum.

which is an *elliptic function* that depends on the parameters E/m (the energy per unit mass) and the length l. However, for our present purpose, it is enough to note that for small oscillations, $\theta \ll 1$, $\sin\theta \approx \theta$ and the equation of motion reduces to

$$\frac{d^2\theta}{dt^2} + \frac{g}{l}\theta = 0, \tag{1.14}$$

which is the equation of motion of a harmonic oscillator with frequency

$$\omega = \sqrt{\frac{g}{l}}.$$

The important fact to notice is that, as long as the oscillations are small, the frequencies of oscillation are constant and independent of the amplitudes: the period of oscillations depends only on the length of the pendulum, as $l^{-1/2}$.

If one expands (1.13) in terms of the amplitude of the pendulum, defined as $l\sin\theta_0$ (where θ_0 is the initial angle at which the pendulum is released), it can be shown from (1.13) with some straightforward algebra that the frequency is

$$\omega = \sqrt{\frac{g}{l}}\left(1 - \frac{1}{16}\theta_0^2 + O(\theta_0^4)\right),$$

in the next order of approximation.

In the general case, the trajectories of the pendulum are as shown in Fig. 1.6. Note that the points with $\theta = 0$ must be identified with those at $\theta = 2\pi$ (that is, the phase space in this problem has the topology of a cylinder: $R_1 \times S_1$). The point $\theta = 0$, $\dot{\theta} = 0$ is a stable equilibrium point and any small deviation leads to small oscillations around it; on the other hand, $\theta = \pi$, $\dot{\theta} = 0$ is an unstable point: it corresponds to the pendulum standing vertically on top of the rigid rod, which is not a stable position. Note also that if the energy is much larger than the gravitational energy, the pendulum rotates with almost constant velocity; in this limiting case (a sling rotating very rapidly as an helix), the gravitational force is negligible.

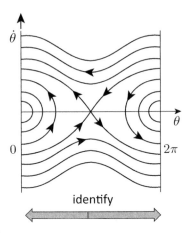

Fig. 1.6. Trajectories in $(\theta, \dot\theta)$ space of the plane pendulum.

1.2.5. *The parachute*

The fall of a parachute can be described with an equation of the form

$$m\frac{dv}{dt} = -mg - \beta v, \tag{1.15}$$

where β is a constant related to the friction of the air. In this simple model, the reasonable assumption is that the friction should be proportional to the velocity. Since x increases with altitude, v is negative during the fall and therefore $-\beta v > 0$ and $-mg < 0$; the two terms in the right-hand side of the above equation are of opposite signs, as it should be: they counterbalance each other.

A first integration of the above equation yields

$$-gt = \int \frac{dv}{1 + (\beta/mg)v}, \tag{1.16}$$

with the solution

$$v(t) = -\frac{mg}{\beta}(1 - e^{-(\beta/m)t}), \tag{1.17}$$

the constant of integration being so chosen that $v = 0$ at time $t = 0$. As expected, the velocity of the parachute tends asymptotically to a finite value, $v \to -mg/\beta$, instead of increasing linearly over time t as if it were a free fall.

A second integration yields

$$x(t) = h_0 + \frac{m^2}{\beta^2} g(1 - e^{-(\beta/m)t}) - \frac{mg}{\beta}t, \qquad (1.18)$$

where h_0 is the initial height of the jump. The time taken to fall to the ground is the solution of this equation with the left-hand side $x(t) = 0$.

1.2.6. *The tautochrone*

As we have seen, the period of oscillation of a pendulum is constant but only if its amplitude is small enough. Such a simple pendulum clearly describes an arc of circle in its plane of motion. Now, the question arises: is there a curve such that a particle moving along it under the influence of gravity oscillates with the same period, independently of the initial amplitude or position? The answer is affirmative: it is a cycloid, also called *tautochrone* (from Greek: *tautos* same, *chronos* time).

A cycloid can be thought of as the curve drawn by a pencil attached to the edge of a wheel rolling along a straight line. An inverted cycloid is shown in Fig. 1.7, described by the parametric equations

$$x = R(\theta - \sin \theta), \quad y = R(1 + \cos \theta), \qquad (1.19)$$

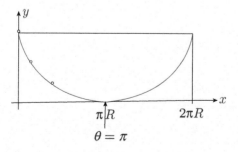

Fig. 1.7. Inverted cycloid.

where θ is a parameter: the cusps of the cycloid correspond to $\theta = 0$ and 2π, and its minimum to $\theta = \pi$ and $x = R\pi$.

Accordingly, the length of a differential section of the cycloid is

$$ds \equiv \sqrt{dx^2 + dy^2} = R\sqrt{2(1 - \cos\theta)}d\theta. \qquad (1.20)$$

Thus, for a particle sliding from rest at height y_0, the energy (per unit mass) is

$$E = \frac{1}{2}\left(\frac{ds}{dt}\right)^2 + gy = gy_0. \qquad (1.21)$$

The simplest way to proceed is to use the trigonometric formulas $1 - \cos\theta = 2\sin^2(\theta/2)$ and $1 + \cos\theta = 2\cos^2(\theta/2)$, and rewrite the energy as

$$E = 2R^2 \sin^2(\theta/2)\dot{\theta}^2 + 2gR\,\cos^2(\theta/2)$$
$$= 8R^2\dot{X}^2 + 2gRX^2, \qquad (1.22)$$

where we have defined the new variable $X = \cos(\theta/2)$. Besides an irrelevant factor $16R^2$ that does not affect the equation of motion, this is exactly the energy of a harmonic oscillator with (squared) frequency $\omega^2 = g/4R$, that is, with period

$$P = 4\pi\sqrt{\frac{R}{g}}, \qquad (1.23)$$

which is independent of the amplitude or initial position θ_0, as it should be!

The involute[4] of a cycloid is also a cycloid. This enabled Christiaan Huygens (1629–1695) to design a very precise pendulum with the bob moving along a cycloid.

1.2.7. *Damped oscillator*

In realistic conditions, an oscillator does not oscillate permanently but undergoes a more or less slow damping due to friction. This

---

[4]Find out what that is.

situation can be modeled with the introduction of an additional term in the basic equation (1.6):

$$\ddot{x} + 2\gamma\dot{x} + \omega^2 x = 0, \tag{1.24}$$

where γ is a *damping coefficient* (with units T^{-1}).

Let us propose a solution of the form

$$x \propto e^{at},$$

where a is a constant. Upon substitution in the above equation, we find that this constant must be a solution of the equation

$$a^2 + 2\gamma a + \omega^2 = 0,$$

and therefore

$$a = -\gamma \pm \sqrt{\gamma^2 - \omega^2}.$$

Thus, we have three possible cases:

(1): $\omega > \gamma$

In this case, $a = -\gamma \pm i\Omega$, where $\Omega = \sqrt{\omega^2 - \gamma^2}$. The general solution is

$$x = e^{-\gamma t}[A\cos(\Omega t) + B\sin(\Omega t)], \tag{1.25}$$

where A and B are constants to be determined by the initial conditions. The above formula represents the oscillatory motion of a particle combined with an exponential damping (see Fig. 1.8). The trajectory in phase space is a spiral tending asymptotically to the rest point $x = 0$ and $\dot{x} = 0$.

(2): $\omega < \gamma$

In this case, a is real and the general solution is

$$x = Ae^{(-\gamma+\sqrt{\gamma^2-\omega^2}\,)t} + Be^{(-\gamma-\sqrt{\gamma^2-\omega^2})t}, \tag{1.26}$$

where A and B are again constants to be determined by the initial conditions. Both exponentials are always negative and thus the two terms decrease exponentially with time. The motion is overdamped: the particle cannot oscillate and simply tends asymptotically to rest.

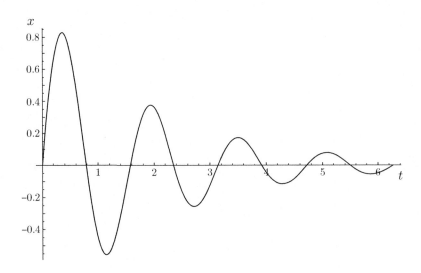

Fig. 1.8. Motion of a damped oscillator.

(3): $\omega = \gamma$.

In this exceptional case, $a = -\gamma$ and we have a general solution of the form

$$x = (A + Bt)e^{-\gamma t}, \tag{1.27}$$

as can be checked by direct substitution. The solution represents a *critical damping* without oscillation.

1.2.8. *Forced oscillator*

Consider now the case of an oscillator subject to an external force, which we assume to be periodic, with a frequency ω_0 and constant amplitude F_0. Then the equation of motion can be written in the form

$$\ddot{x} + 2\gamma\dot{x} + \omega^2 x = F_0 e^{i\omega_0 t}. \tag{1.28}$$

Let us propose the solution

$$x = A e^{i\omega_0 t},$$

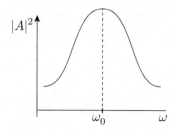

Fig. 1.9. Amplitude of a forced oscillator as a function of frequency.

where A is a constant complex amplitude. Upon substitution in the above equation, we find

$$A(-\omega_0^2 + 2i\gamma\omega_0 + \omega^2) = F_0.$$

The magnitude of the amplitude A is then

$$|A|^2 = \frac{|F_0|^2}{(\omega^2 - \omega_0^2)^2 + 4\gamma^2}. \qquad (1.29)$$

The graph of $|A|^2$ as a function of ω is shown in Fig. 1.9. The interpretation of this result is as follows: the amplitude of the oscillations produced by the external force has a maximum if the frequency ω of the oscillator coincides with the frequency ω_0 of the external force. This is known as a *resonance effect*. In general, a solid body or any mechanical system (see the last section in this chapter) has inherently one or more frequencies of oscillation (normal modes); an external force acting on it with the same frequency as one of these internal frequencies can produce a rupture (find out what happened to the Broughton bridge and why soldiers should not march while on bridges).

1.2.9. *Parametric oscillator*

A particularly interesting case is that of an oscillator with a time-varying frequency. The general equation is

$$\ddot{x} + \omega^2(t)x = 0, \qquad (1.30)$$

where, in most relevant cases, the frequency $\omega(t)$ itself oscillates around a certain value.

As a realistic physical example, consider the problem of an electrically charged particle in a potential of the form

$$\Phi = \frac{F(t)}{r_0^2}(\alpha x^2 + \beta y^2 + \gamma z^2),$$

where α, β, γ, and r_0 are constants, and $F(t)$ is a function that depends on time. This potential must satisfy the Laplace equation[5]

$$\nabla^2 \Phi = 0,$$

and therefore

$$\alpha + \beta + \gamma = 0,$$

which implies that these three constants cannot have the same sign. A typical form of the potential could be

$$\Phi = \frac{F}{r_0^2}(x^2 + y^2 - 2z^2).$$

Now, the force applied on a particle of mass m and charge e is $\mathbf{F} = -e\nabla\Phi$ and therefore the equations of motion are

$$m\ddot{x} = -2e\frac{F}{r_0^2}x,$$

$$m\ddot{y} = -2e\frac{F}{r_0^2}y, \tag{1.31}$$

$$m\ddot{z} = 4e\frac{F}{r_0^2}z.$$

The first two equations correspond to the usual harmonic oscillators, but the third is the equation of an inverted oscillator. Thus, if F is constant, the motion of the particle may be stable along the x and y directions, but it is unstable in the third direction. In a three-dimensional graph, the potential looks like a saddle (Fig. 1.10) and there is a "saddle-point instability" at the origin; in fact, no point in the potential is stable.

---

[5]The same equation applies to a gravitational force; see the following chapter.

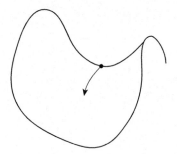

Fig. 1.10. "Saddle" type potential.

Nevertheless, one can choose F to be time-dependent, for instance,

$$F(t) = U + V\cos(\Omega t),$$

where U and V are constants. With some straightforward algebra, the equation of motion in the z direction takes the form

$$\frac{d^2z}{dv^2} + [a - 2q\cos(2v)]z = 0, \qquad (1.32)$$

where $a = -16eU/mr_0^2\Omega^2$ and $q = 16eV/mr_0^2\Omega^2$, and v is a dimensionless coordinate defined as $2v = \Omega t$. An entirely similar equation applies for the x and y coordinates, but with $a = 8eU/mr_0^2\Omega^2$ and $q = -4eV/mr_0^2\Omega^2$.

The above equation is the standard form of the *Mathieu equation*. It is known that this equation has stable and unstable solutions depending on the values of the parameters a and q. In Fig. 1.11, the regions of stability and instability are depicted in a (a, q) plane. It can be seen that there are values of these parameters for which the equations of motion admit stable solutions. Thus, by properly choosing these parameters, it is possible to keep a charged particle in a stable position in an oscillating electric field. This is how a *Paul trap* works, designed for trapping ions and electrons.[6]

---

[6]Invented by Wolfgang Paul (1913–1993), who received the Nobel Prize in Physics in 1989.

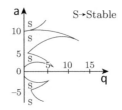

Fig. 1.11. Regions of stability and instability of the Mathieu equation.

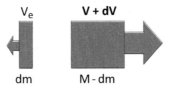

Fig. 1.12. Graphical motion of a rocket.

Another application of the Mathieu equation will be worked out in Section 6.3.4 of Chapter 6 for the problem of the inverted pendulum.

1.3. Variable mass: The rocket

So far, we have studied the motion of particles with constant mass. However, Newton's second law, which relates force to the change of momentum (mass times velocity), is not restricted to constant masses. A typical problem involving a time-varying mass is that of a rocket.

A rocket moves thanks to Newton's third law: by the conservation of momentum, it moves forward by burning and ejecting fuel backwards. Suppose the rocket is launched vertically from ground with an initial mass $m(0)$ of fuel and payload, and with velocity $v(0) = 0$. At a certain time t after the launch, part of its fuel has been burned, its mass has reduced to $m(t)$ and its velocity $v(t)$ has increased. Thus, if the rocket ejects a mass dm backwards at time t, its velocity increases to $v + dv$ at time $t + dt$, as depicted in Fig. 1.12.

Now, let V_e be the velocity of the ejected mass with respect to the moving rocket (not to the ground). If V_e is constant, the conservation of the momentum $p(t) = m(t)v(t)$ implies

$$p(t + dt) = (m - dm)(v + dv) + (v - V_e)dm.$$

It then follows that

$$dp(t) \equiv p(t + dt) - p(t) = m\,dv + V_e\,dm,$$

and therefore

$$\frac{dp}{dt} = m(t)\frac{dv}{dt} + V_e\frac{dm(t)}{dt}, \tag{1.33}$$

which must be equal, by Newton's second law, to the gravitational force applied to the rocket, that is, $dp/dt = -m(t)g$. It can be easily checked that the solution of the resulting equation is

$$v(t) = V_e \ln\left(\frac{m_0}{m(t)}\right) - gt, \tag{1.34}$$

where $m_0 = m(0)$ is the initial total mass of the rocket (fuel plus engines and cabin) at launch time $t = 0$.

If the rocket is moving freely in space far from a gravitational field, $g = 0$, its velocity increases logarithmically and its final velocity, after exhausting all its fuel, will be

$$v_{fin} = V_e \ln\left(\frac{m_0}{m_{fin}}\right), \tag{1.35}$$

where m_{fin} is the final mass of the rocket (its payload). We see that the final velocity is of the same order of magnitude as the ejection velocity and increases only logarithmically with the quantity of fuel carried on. This is due to the fact that an increase in the load of fuel also requires an increase in the energy necessary to carry it! A standard rocket is a rather inefficient way of traveling through space.

1.4. Two- and three-dimensional problems

Let us now consider the motion of a particle in a two- or three-dimensional space. In these cases, it is not always possible to obtain the force from a scalar potential. The general condition for the existence of a potential $U(\mathbf{r})$ such that $\mathbf{F} = -\nabla U(\mathbf{r})$ is that the rotational of the force vanishes: $\nabla \times \mathbf{F} = 0$. Thus, for instance, a force of the form $\mathbf{F} = (-y, x, 0)$ cannot be the gradient of a scalar potential. Fortunately, most important forces are potential, such as the central force to be studied in the following.

An important property of potential forces is that the work performed by a particle in going from point 1 to point 2 is independent of the trajectory: the force is said to be *conservative*. Indeed, the work is defined as

$$W_{12} = \int_1^2 \mathbf{F} \cdot d\mathbf{r}, \tag{1.36}$$

with the integration taken along a particular trajectory from 1 to 2. Now, the difference of the works performed along two distinct trajectories with the same initial and final points turns out to be the work performed along a closed loop, as seen in Fig. 1.13. Explicitly,

$$W_{12} - W'_{12} = \oint \mathbf{F} \cdot d\mathbf{r} = -\iint (\nabla \times \mathbf{F}) \cdot d\mathbf{S}, \tag{1.37}$$

using the Stokes theorem.[7] Therefore $W_{12} = W'_{12}$ for a conservative force.

Note also that in two or three dimensions, the phase space has four or six dimensions, respectively. This cannot be represented visually, though it may be described mathematically.

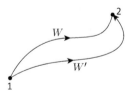

Fig. 1.13. Trajectories in the field of a conservative force.

---

[7] $\iint (\nabla \times \mathbf{F}) \cdot d\mathbf{S} = \oint \mathbf{F} \cdot d\mathbf{r}$, where $d\mathbf{S}$ is an element of surface and $d\mathbf{r}$ an element of length.

1.4.1. *Angular momentum*

Angular momentum is a very important concept in mechanics. Given the momentum $\mathbf{p}$ of a particle located at the position $\mathbf{r}$ with respect to the origin of a given coordinate system, the angular momentum is defined as

$$\mathbf{L} = \mathbf{r} \times \mathbf{p}. \tag{1.38}$$

Since $\dot{\mathbf{p}} = m\dot{\mathbf{v}} = \mathbf{F}$ and $\dot{\mathbf{r}} = \mathbf{v}$, the time derivative of $\mathbf{L}$ reduces, by Newton's second law, to

$$\frac{d}{dt}\mathbf{L} = \mathbf{r} \times \mathbf{F} \equiv \mathbf{K}, \tag{1.39}$$

thus defining the *torque* $\mathbf{K} = \mathbf{r} \times \mathbf{F}$.

In the important case of a central force, $\mathbf{F} \propto \mathbf{r}$, the torque is zero and the angular momentum $\mathbf{L}$ turns out to be a constant of motion. Moreover, since $\mathbf{r} \cdot \mathbf{L} = 0$, the motion of a particle is restricted to a constant plane perpendicular to $\mathbf{L}$. Such a plane is also defined by the initial position $\mathbf{r}$ and velocity $\mathbf{v}$ vectors. Thus, the motion in a central force field can be taken, without any loss of generality, as a two-dimensional motion. This fact will be used in the following chapter.

Another important result is that the angular momentum must be directly related to the velocity of the area swept out by the position vector of a particle. Indeed, from Fig. 1.14, it is evident that the increase of area in a time interval dt is

$$dA = \frac{1}{2}|\mathbf{r} \times \mathbf{v}|dt,$$

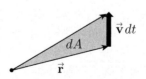

Fig. 1.14. Illustration of Kepler's second law.

and therefore

$$\frac{dA}{dt} = \frac{1}{2m}|\mathbf{L}|. \tag{1.40}$$

If $\mathbf{L}$ is constant, the complete area A enclosed by the orbit is $A = (1/2m)|\mathbf{L}|P$, where P is the period of a full cycle. In this case, Kepler's second law follows: "A line segment joining a planet and the Sun sweeps out equal areas in equal times".

This problem will be considered in more detail in the following chapter.

1.4.2. *Harmonic oscillators*

Consider the problem of a harmonic oscillator in a two-dimensional plane: a particle of mass m subject to a single spring fixed at the origin and with the Hooke constant k. The equations of motion are

$$\ddot{x} + \omega^2 x = 0,$$
$$\ddot{y} + \omega^2 y = 0, \tag{1.41}$$

($\omega^2 = k/m$ as usual) with an obvious solution

$$x = a\cos(\omega t - \alpha),$$
$$y = b\sin(\omega t - \alpha), \tag{1.42}$$

which is an ellipse with semiaxes a and b, and with α an arbitrary angle. The angular momentum L is constant since

$$\frac{d}{dt}(x\dot{y} - y\dot{x}) = 0,$$

and therefore $L = mab\omega$. Since the area of an ellipse is πab, the period of revolution is $2\pi/\omega$ according to Eq. (1.40). As for the total energy, it is $E = \frac{1}{2}m^2\omega^2(a^2 + b^2)$.

The problem of a particle subject to two perpendicular springs with *different* Hooke constants is illustrative of the use of phase spaces in higher dimensions. The trajectories in phase space are given by

$$E = \frac{m}{2}(v_x^2 + v_y^2) + \frac{1}{2}(k_x x^2 + k_y y^2), \qquad (1.43)$$

thus the particle is constrained to a "hyper-ellipsoid" in a four-dimensional phase space and cannot go beyond a surface corresponding to zero velocity, $v_x = 0 = v_y$. Such a surface of zero-velocity is the ellipse

$$E = \frac{1}{2}(k_x x^2 + k_y y^2),$$

and it is the boundary of all possible trajectories of the two-dimensional harmonic oscillator. Moreover, the energy can be decoupled into two parts, $E = E_x + E_y$, where

$$E_x = \frac{1}{2}(mv_x^2 + k_x x^2), \quad E_y = \frac{1}{2}(mv_y^2 + k_y y^2),$$

and therefore

$$x \leq \sqrt{2E_x/k_x} \equiv A_x, \quad y \leq \sqrt{2E_y/k_y} \equiv A_y.$$

The conclusion is that the particle is restricted to move inside the rectangle with sides A_x and A_y.

In the particular case $k_x = k_y = k$, the equations of motion are (1.41), with the general solution (1.42): the trajectories are ellipses with frequency $\sqrt{k/m}$.

If $k_x \neq k_y$, but the ratio k_x/k_y is a rational number, the trajectories are *Lissajous* figures, as shown in Fig. 1.15. Otherwise, the trajectories do not close but fill the whole plane inside the rectangle with sides A_x and A_y.

1.4.3. *The spherical pendulum*

In three-dimensional space, a spherical pendulum moves on the surface of a sphere. Clearly, the natural coordinates for this problem

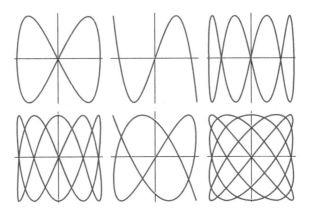

Fig. 1.15. Lissajous trajectories.

are the spherical coordinates (r, θ, ϕ), defined as

$$x = r \cos \theta \cos \phi,$$
$$y = r \cos \theta \sin \phi, \tag{1.44}$$
$$z = r \sin \theta.$$

Distances are measured with the line element

$$ds^2 = dr^2 + r^2 \, d\theta^2 + r^2 \sin^2 \theta \, d\phi^2. \tag{1.45}$$

If the length R of the pendulum is constant, we must set $r = R$, and its position is thus described by the two coordinates (θ, ϕ). The magnitude of the velocity is $ds/dt = R(\dot\theta^2 + \sin \theta \, \dot\phi^2)^{1/2}$ and the energy (per unit mass) of the pendulum is

$$E = \frac{1}{2} R^2 (\dot\theta^2 + \sin^2 \theta \, \dot\phi^2) + gR \cos \theta \tag{1.46}$$

(θ is the angle between the vertical and the pendulum). The velocity vector has two components and is given by

$$\mathbf{v} = R(\dot\theta \hat{\mathbf{e}}_\theta + \sin \theta \, \dot\phi \hat{\mathbf{e}}_\phi),$$

where $\hat{\mathbf{e}}_\theta$ and $\hat{\mathbf{e}}_\phi$ are the unit vectors in the directions of increasing θ and ϕ (as we will see in more detail in Section 2.2 of Chapter 2).

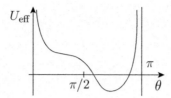

Fig. 1.16. The effective potential function U_{eff} of a spherical pendulum.

Now, the force $\mathbf{F}$ acting on the pendulum is vertical and therefore the torque $\mathbf{r} \times \mathbf{F}$ is in the $\hat{\mathbf{e}}_\phi$ direction. This means that the component of the angular momentum vector in the $\hat{\mathbf{e}}_\theta$ direction is constant, in accordance with the discussion in Section 1.4.1. The angular momentum (per unit mass) is $\mathbf{l} = \mathbf{r} \times \mathbf{v}$ and its θ component is $l = R^2 \sin^2 \theta \, \dot{\phi}$, which is constant. Thus, we can rewrite the energy (1.46) in the form

$$E = \frac{1}{2} R^2 \dot{\theta}^2 + U_{\text{eff}}, \tag{1.47}$$

where the effective potential is defined as

$$U_{\text{eff}} = \frac{l^2}{2R^2 \sin^2 \theta} - gR \cos \theta. \tag{1.48}$$

A graph of this function for a typical value of l is shown in Fig. 1.16. It is seen that for a given value of the energy, the motion of the pendulum is restricted between two values of θ. Clearly, for $l = 0$, we recover the plane pendulum.

1.5. Normal modes

Let us now consider, as an illustrative problem, a system of two or more coupled oscillators. For instance, two particles, each of mass m, are bound together and moving along the x axis, as shown in Fig. 1.17.

Let x_1 and x_2 be the coordinates of the particles, with $x_1 = 0$ and $x_2 = 0$ being their equilibrium positions. Let also k be the Hooke coefficient of each of the three springs, as shown in Fig. 1.17. Each

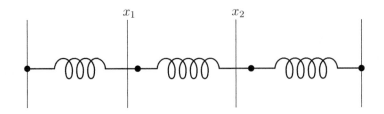

$$x_1 \qquad x_2$$

Fig. 1.17. Coupled oscillators.

lateral spring has one of its ends fixed and the equations of motion turn out to be

$$m\ddot{x}_1 = -kx_1 - k(x_1 + x_2),$$
$$m\ddot{x}_2 = -kx_2 - k(x_1 + x_2). \tag{1.49}$$

We can take as solutions of these equations:

$$x_1 = A_1 e^{i\omega t}, \quad x_2 = A_2 e^{i\omega t}, \tag{1.50}$$

(with A_i constants) and the equations of motion imply, in a matrix form,

$$\begin{pmatrix} -m\omega^2 + 2k & k \\ k & -m\omega^2 + 2k \end{pmatrix} \begin{pmatrix} A_1 \\ A_2 \end{pmatrix} = 0. \tag{1.51}$$

This matrix equation has non-trivial solutions if its determinant is zero, which means that

$$\omega^4 - 4\omega_0^2 \omega^2 + 3\omega_0^2 = 0, \tag{1.52}$$

where $\omega_0^2 = k/m$. The two solutions are

$$\omega^2 = 3\omega_0^2, \quad \omega^2 = \omega_0^2,$$

which are the frequencies of the two *normal modes* of this particular system. The first mode corresponds to $A_1 = A_2$ and the second to $A_1 = -A_1$. In the first case, the two masses oscillate together in the same direction with frequency $\sqrt{3}\omega_0$. In the second case, they oscillate in opposite directions to each other with frequencies ω_0.

In general, the motion of the two particles is a superposition of the two normal modes

$$X_\pm = x_1 \pm x_2,$$

with frequencies $\omega_+ = \sqrt{3}\omega_0$ and $\omega_- = \omega_0$. They satisfy the decoupled pair of equations

$$\ddot{X}_\pm + \omega_\pm^2 X_\pm = 0,$$

with obvious solutions.

Of course, in this simple example, the same results above can be obtained by summing and subtracting the two equations in (1.50).

1.5.1. *The double pendulum*

Consider a double pendulum, each of mass m_i and length l_i, as depicted in Fig. 1.18, oscillating in the (x, y) plane. The position of each bob is

$$\mathbf{r_1} = l_1(\cos\theta_1, \sin\theta_1),$$
$$\mathbf{r_2} = \mathbf{r_1} + l_2(\cos\theta_2, \sin\theta_2),$$

$$(1.53)$$

and the velocity vectors are accordingly

$$\mathbf{v_1} = l_1(-\sin\theta_1, \cos\theta_1)\dot{\theta}_1,$$
$$\mathbf{v_2} = \mathbf{v_1} + l_2(-\sin\theta_2, \cos\theta_2)\dot{\theta}_2.$$

$$(1.54)$$

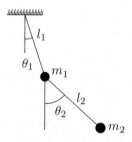

Fig. 1.18. The double pendulum.

It then follows that the total energy of the system is

$$E = \frac{1}{2}m_1 l_1^2 \dot{\theta}_1^2 + \frac{1}{2}m_2[l_1^2 \dot{\theta}_1^2 + l_2^2 \dot{\theta}_2^2 + 2l_1 l_2 \cos(\theta_1 - \theta_2)\dot{\theta}_1\dot{\theta}_2]$$
$$- (m_1 + m_2)gl_1 \cos\theta_1 - m_2 gl_2 \cos\theta_2. \tag{1.55}$$

In the limit of small oscillations, $\theta_i \ll 1$, the equations of motion reduce with some straightforward algebra to

$$l_1\ddot{\theta}_1 + \mu l_2\ddot{\theta}_2 + g\theta_1 = 0, \tag{1.56}$$

$$l_1\ddot{\theta}_1 + l_2\ddot{\theta}_2 + g\theta_2 = 0, \tag{1.57}$$

where

$$\mu = \frac{m_1}{m_1 + m_2}.$$

If we now propose the solution

$$\theta_i = A_i e^{i\omega t},$$

we get the matrix equation

$$\begin{pmatrix} g - l_1\omega^2 & -\mu l_2\omega^2 \\ -l_1\omega^2 & g - l_2\omega^2 \end{pmatrix} \begin{pmatrix} A_1 \\ A_2 \end{pmatrix} = 0. \tag{1.58}$$

This system of equations has non-trivial solutions if the determinant of its matrix is zero, namely

$$l_1 l_2(1 - \mu)\omega^4 - g(l_1 + l_2)\omega^2 + g^2 = 0. \tag{1.59}$$

The general solution can be obtained by simple algebra, but it is not very illustrative. Let us rather consider the simple case of two identical pendulums, $m_1 = m_2 = m$ and $l_1 = l_2 = l$, hanging one on the other. Then the above equation has the two solutions

$$\omega^2 = \frac{g}{l}(2 \pm \sqrt{2}) \equiv \omega_\pm^2, \tag{1.60}$$

and accordingly we have two possibilities for the amplitudes of oscillation:

$$A_1 = \mp\sqrt{2}A_2,$$

corresponding to the two bobs oscillating in opposite directions (+ sign) or in the same directions (− sign).

We can write the solution of the problem in terms of the two normal modes:

$$\Theta_\pm = \sqrt{2}\theta_1 \mp \theta_2. \tag{1.61}$$

These normal modes satisfy the two decoupled equations

$$\ddot{\Theta}_\pm + \omega_\pm^2 \Theta_\pm = 0,$$

as it is the case of normal modes.

By now, the method of obtaining the normal modes of a mechanical system should be obvious and can be extended to any number of particles.

1.6. The vibrating string

In this section, we deduce the equation describing the vibration of a string as it follows from Newton's second law. For this purpose, we consider a small section of a string in the plane (x, Y) subject to two forces at its extremes, as shown in Fig. 1.19. The string is displaced from its rest position which coincides with the x axis.

If τ is the force of tension of the string, the x and Y components of the net force (F_x, F_Y) acting on that small section of length Δs are

$$F_x = \tau \cos\theta(x + \Delta x) - \tau \cos\theta(x), \tag{1.62}$$

$$F_Y = \tau \sin\theta(x + \Delta x) - \tau \sin\theta(x), \tag{1.63}$$

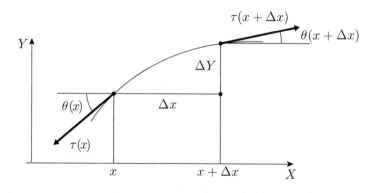

Fig. 1.19. The vibrating string.

where $\theta(x)$ is the angle between the string and the x axis at the position with coordinate x (see Fig. 1.19).

This last pair of formulas is exact, but in most practical cases, the transverse displacement of a string is extremely small (think of any string instrument), and accordingly the angle θ is very small. Thus, since $\sin\theta \approx \theta$ and $\cos\theta \approx 1 - \theta^2/2$, the component F_x is of second order in θ and can be safely neglected; the component F_Y is the only relevant one. As for the slope of the string, it can be approximated as

$$\frac{\partial Y}{\partial x}(x,t) = \tan\theta(x,t) \approx \theta(x,t).$$

Note that the displacement $Y(x,t)$ must be taken as a function of both x and t.

Now, the force in the Y direction is

$$F_Y \approx \tau\theta(x+\Delta x) - \tau\theta(x)$$
$$\approx \tau\left[\frac{\partial Y(x+\Delta x)}{\partial x} - \frac{\partial Y(x)}{\partial x}\right]$$
$$\approx \tau\frac{\partial^2 Y}{\partial x^2}\Delta x. \tag{1.64}$$

On the other hand, according to Newton's second law, that same force is

$$F_Y = \sigma\Delta s\frac{\partial^2 Y}{\partial t^2},$$

where σ is the mass per unit length of the string. Since $\Delta s \approx \Delta x$ in a first-order approximation, we can combine these two last equations for the force F_Y and obtain the (one-dimensional) wave equation

$$\frac{1}{v_s^2}\frac{\partial^2 Y}{\partial t^2} - \frac{\partial^2 Y}{\partial x^2} = 0, \tag{1.65}$$

where

$$v_s \equiv \sqrt{\frac{T}{\sigma}}$$

is the velocity of transmission of a signal along the string.

The above equation (1.65) is a typical wave equation of which there are many applications in physics and engineering. In its present one-dimensional form, it can be easily solved defining new variables

$$\zeta_\pm = v_s t \pm x.$$

The equation then takes the form

$$\frac{\partial^2 Y}{\partial \zeta_+ \, \partial \zeta_-} = 0,$$

with the obvious solution

$$Y(t, x) = Y_-(v_s t - x) + Y_+(v_s t + x). \tag{1.66}$$

The first (second) term represents a wave running along the positive (negative) x direction with velocity v_s and without altering its original shape.

The situation is different if boundary conditions are imposed on the string. In this case, it is convenient to solve the wave equation (1.65) by separation of variables setting

$$Y(x, t) = X(x)\, T(t), \tag{1.67}$$

and thus,

$$\ddot{T} + \omega^2 T = 0, \quad v_s^2 X'' + \omega^2 X = 0, \tag{1.68}$$

where ω^2 is a separation constant: ω is the frequency of oscillation of the string.

If a string of length L is fixed at its extremes $x = 0$ and $x = L$, the boundary conditions are

$$X(0) = 0 = X(L).$$

It is straight forward to check that the solution satisfying the correct boundary conditions is $Y(x, t) = \sum_n Y_n(x, t)$, with

$$Y_n(x, t) = \sin \frac{n\pi x}{L} \left[A_n \sin \frac{n\pi v_s}{L} t + B_n \cos \frac{n\pi v_s}{L} t \right], \tag{1.69}$$

where A_n and B_n are constants, and the frequency of oscillation ω is such

$$\omega = \frac{n\pi v_s}{L},$$

in terms of an integer number n. This last condition implies that the frequency ω is "quantized" in the sense that it can only take integer values of a *fundamental frequency*

$$\omega_f = \frac{\pi v_s}{L}.$$

An octave is the interval between one musical note and another with double or half its frequency. A longer length L of the spring produces a lower pitch and vice versa. Musicians can control the pitch changing manually the length of the string between its fixed end positions. In Western music, the commonly used tuning system is a set of 12 notes obtained by multiplying (or dividing) successively the frequency of the basic note **A** (440 Hz) by a factor $2^{1/12} \approx 1.05946\ldots$; in this way, a complete octave is covered.

Chapter 2

Newtonian Gravity

Newton's law of gravity specifies that two masses, m_1 and m_2, attract each other with a force

$$\mathbf{F} = -\frac{Gm_1m_2}{r^2}\mathbf{e_r},\qquad(2.1)$$

where r is the distance between the two masses, $\mathbf{e_r} = \mathbf{r}/r$ is the unit vector in the radial direction uniting them, and Newton's constant G has the experimentally measured value $6.674 \times 10^{-11}\,\mathrm{N\,m^2/kg^2}$.

2.1. Gravitational potential

Since inertial and gravitational masses are equal, as it is known from Galileo's time, the gravitational acceleration of a particle does not depend on its mass: all bodies fall with the same acceleration. This is known as the *equivalence principle*.[1] Accordingly, the acceleration of any particle produced by a mass m is Gm/r^2, which[2] can be deduced from a *potential by unit mass*

$$\Phi(r) = -\frac{Gm}{r}.\qquad(2.2)$$

Thus, the force on a particle with mass m' is $\mathbf{F} = -m'\nabla\Phi(r)$.

Newton's law of gravity is valid for point masses. An important question is whether it also applies to any distribution of mass.

---

[1] In comparison, there is no such equivalence between the inertial mass and the electrical charge of a body.

[2] On the surface of the Earth, $g = GM/R^2$, M is the mass of the Earth and R its radius; $g \approx 9.8\,\mathrm{m/s^2}$.

In order to elucidate this point, we first note that the gravitational force is lineal, in the sense that the total attractive force of various masses is just the vectorial sum of each of the forces separately.[3] Accordingly, the potential produced at the position $\mathbf{r}$ by various point masses m_i located each at $\mathbf{r}_i$ is

$$\Phi(\mathbf{r}) = -\sum_i \frac{Gm_i}{|\mathbf{r} - \mathbf{r}_i|}, \tag{2.3}$$

where the sum is taken over all particles. The continuous version of this formula is

$$\Phi(\mathbf{r}) = -G \int \frac{\rho(\mathbf{r}')}{|\mathbf{r} - \mathbf{r}'|} dV', \tag{2.4}$$

where the integration is over the volume occupied by a body of *mass density* $\rho(\mathbf{r})$.

Let us calculate the gravitational force exerted by a spherically symmetric massive body. As a first step, we calculate the potential of a spherical thin shell of radius r' and uniform mass σ per unit area. The mass of the shell is then $m = 4\pi\sigma r'^2$. As can be seen from Fig. 2.1, the potential of the shell at a distance r from its center is

$$\Phi(r) = -2\pi G\sigma \int_0^\pi \frac{r'^2 \sin\theta}{l(\theta, r, r')} d\theta, \tag{2.5}$$

where

$$l(\theta; r, r') = \sqrt{r'^2 + r^2 - 2r'r\cos\theta}.$$

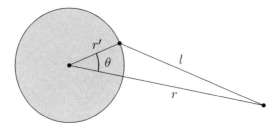

Fig. 2.1. Gravitational attraction of a shell.

---

[3]This is also the case of classical electrodynamics, but not of quantum electrodynamics nor of the general relativistic theory of gravitation.

The above integral can be easily performed changing from the variable of integration θ to the new variable $l(\theta)$, with the result

$$\Phi(r > r') = -2\pi G\sigma \frac{r'}{r} \int_{r-r'}^{r+r'} dl = -\frac{Gm}{r}, \qquad (2.6)$$

if $r > r'$, that is, if the point r is outside the shell. However, if $r' > r$,

$$\Phi(r < r') = -2\pi G\sigma \frac{r'}{r} \int_{r'-r}^{r'+r} dl = -\frac{Gm}{r'}. \qquad (2.7)$$

Thus, the potential *outside* the shell is identical to the potential of a point particle with the same mass at its center, but it is constant *inside* the shell. This means that there is no gravitational force inside a spherically symmetric homogeneous shell of matter.

With this result in hand, imagine a spherical massive body which is a superposition of spherical cells (like an onion!). Since each cell attracts outside it as if its mass were concentrated at its center, we can deduce that the gravitational force exerted by a spherically symmetric distribution of mass is identical to the gravitational force due to a point mass located at the center of the sphere. Thus, we are justified in considering the Earth or any planet as a point mass in most practical applications. A deviation from spherical symmetry would produce a correction to the potential that decays as r^{-2} or faster, as we will see in Section 2.3 on multipolar expansions.

2.1.1. *Trapped neutrino*

The neutrino is a (ghost-like!) particle that does not interact electromagnetically with other particles, but is subject to gravity. Suppose a neutrino is trapped inside the Earth by its gravitational attraction. What is the trajectory of the neutrino?

According to the previous discussion, the gravitational force inside the Earth at a distance r from its center is

$$-\frac{GM(r)}{r^2},$$

where $M(r)$ is the mass inside a spherical section of the Earth with radius r. If we suppose for simplicity that the density is constant, then $M(r) = Mr^3/R^3$, where R is the radius of the Earth and M its total mass. Accordingly, the force on the neutrino is

$$-\frac{GM}{R^3}r,$$

which is the force applied to a two-dimensional harmonic oscillator. This problem has already been considered in Section 1.4.1 of Chapter 1: the trajectory is an ellipse and the orbital period is $2\pi\sqrt{R^3/GM}$, which turns out to be about 84 minutes.

2.1.2. *Escape velocity*

What is the minimum initial velocity that a cannonball fired vertically must have to escape from the gravitational attraction of the Earth[4] or any planet? It is enough to note that the total energy (per unit mass) of a body moving radially with respect to the center of a planet with mass M is

$$E = \frac{1}{2}v^2 - \frac{GM}{r}.$$

Accordingly, in order for a cannonball or any object to reach infinity at least with zero velocity, that is, energy $E = 0$, its initial velocity must be at least

$$v_{esc} = \sqrt{\frac{2GM}{R}}, \tag{2.8}$$

where R is the radius of the planet; otherwise, with a smaller velocity, it will reach a certain altitude and fall back. This velocity is 11.19 km/s for the Earth, 617 km/s for the Sun, and 2.4 km/s for the Moon. The escape velocity is equal to the velocity of light for a "black hole", a body with a mass M and radius $2GM/c^2$, which amounts to about 3 km for each solar mass.

2.2. The Kepler problem

We are now ready to analyze the problem of planetary motion. Let us first suppose for simplicity that the Sun (or any attracting body) is

---

[4]As in Jules Verne's novel *From the Earth to the Moon*.

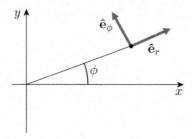

Fig. 2.2. Radial coordinates.

much more massive than the planet (or, in general, a particle) whose motion we want to study (the two-bodies problem will be studied in Section 3.2.1 of Chapter 3).

As explained in the previous chapter, the conservation of angular momentum for a radial force implies that the motion of the planet remains in a plane, so we can restrict the analysis to a two-dimensional space. When dealing with a motion in two dimensions, we can use polar coordinates (r, ϕ), defined as (see Fig. 2.2)

$$x = r \cos \phi, \quad y = r \sin \phi, \tag{2.9}$$

in terms of the Cartesian coordinates (x, y). The corresponding unitary vectors (see Fig. 2.2) are related to the Cartesian unitary vectors $\mathbf{e}_x$ and $\mathbf{e}_y$ through the relations

$$\mathbf{e}_r = \cos \phi \, \mathbf{e}_x + \sin \phi \, \mathbf{e}_y, \quad \mathbf{e}_\phi = -\sin \phi \, \mathbf{e}_x + \cos \phi \, \mathbf{e}_y, \tag{2.10}$$

as it can be seen from the same figure.

Unlike the Cartesian unitary vectors, those associated to polar coordinates are not constant vectors. Actually, the last formulas imply

$$d\mathbf{e}_r = \mathbf{e}_\phi \, d\phi, \quad d\mathbf{e}_\phi = -\mathbf{e}_r \, d\phi. \tag{2.11}$$

In particular, the position vector is just $\mathbf{r} \equiv r\mathbf{e}_r$, and thus, the velocity is

$$\dot{\mathbf{r}} \equiv \mathbf{v} = \mathbf{e}_r \dot{r} + r\dot{\phi}\mathbf{e}_\phi, \tag{2.12}$$

and therefore,

$$v^2 = \dot{r}^2 + r^2\dot{\phi}^2. \tag{2.13}$$

Accordingly, the magnitude of the angular momentum (per unit mass) $\mathbf{r} \times \mathbf{v}$ turns out to be

$$l = r^2\dot{\phi}, \tag{2.14}$$

which is a constant.

Thus, returning to our planet, its energy (per unit mass) is

$$\begin{aligned}
E &= \frac{1}{2}(\dot{r}^2 + r^2\dot{\phi}^2) - \frac{GM}{r} \\
&= \frac{1}{2}\dot{r}^2 + \frac{l^2}{2r^2} - \frac{GM}{r}.
\end{aligned} \tag{2.15}$$

This suggests to define an effective potential

$$U_{\text{eff}}(r) = \frac{l^2}{2r^2} - \frac{GM}{r},$$

such that $E = \frac{1}{2}\dot{r}^2 + U_{\text{eff}}(r)$. The graph of the function $U_{\text{eff}}(r)$ is shown in Fig. 2.3.

Furthermore, since

$$\frac{dr}{dt} = \sqrt{2[E - U_{\text{eff}}(r)]}, \tag{2.16}$$

and $l = r^2\, d\phi/dt$, we have

$$l\frac{dr}{d\phi} = r^2\sqrt{2[E - U_{\text{eff}}(r)]}. \tag{2.17}$$

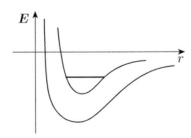

Fig. 2.3. Potential with angular momentum term.

Changing to a new variable $u = 1/r$, this last equation takes the following form with some simple algebra:

$$\frac{d^2u}{d\phi^2} + u = \frac{Gm}{l^2}, \tag{2.18}$$

with the solution

$$u = \frac{GM}{l^2}(1 + e\cos\phi), \tag{2.19}$$

where e is a constant to be identified in the following.

There are three possible cases depending on the sign of the energy E.

Case $E < 0$: If the energy E is negative, the orbits are bound. For a given value of the angular momentum l, the particle is constrained to move inside the boundaries corresponding to null radial velocity $\dot{r}$, as shown in Fig. 2.3. The maximum and minimum distances from the center (*aphelion* and *perihelion* for planets in the solar system), r_+ and r_-, are

$$r_\pm = \frac{GM}{2|E|} \pm \sqrt{\left(\frac{GM}{2|E|}\right)^2 - \frac{l^2}{2|E|}}. \tag{2.20}$$

If the solution (2.19) is substituted in (2.17), it results that

$$\cos\phi = \left(\frac{l}{r} - \frac{GM}{l}\right) \bigg/ \sqrt{(GM/l)^2 - 2|E|}, \tag{2.21}$$

as can be checked by direct substitution. It is convenient to rewrite this last formula as

$$r = \frac{p}{1 + e\cos\phi}, \tag{2.22}$$

which is the equation of an ellipse, as shown in Fig. 2.4, with eccentricity

$$e = \sqrt{1 - 2|E|l^2/(GM)^2}, \tag{2.23}$$

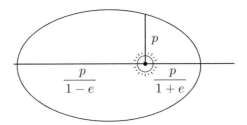

Fig. 2.4. Orbital parameters.

and *semi-latus rectum*

$$p = \frac{l^2}{GM};$$
(2.24)

compare with (2.19). The perihelion and aphelion of the orbit correspond to $\phi = 0$ and $\phi = \pi$, respectively.

Thus, for bound orbits, $E < 0$ and $0 \le e < 1$, the orbits are ellipses with semi-major axis

$$a = \frac{p}{1 - e^2},$$

and semi-minor axis

$$b = \frac{p}{\sqrt{1 - e^2}},$$

with one of the foci at the origin. An eccentricity $e = 0$ corresponds to circular orbits of radius $r = l^2/GM$ (at the minimum of the curve $U_{\text{eff}}(r)$), with energy $E = -\frac{1}{2}(GM/l)^2$.

The orbital period P can be deduced directly from Kepler's second law: integrating Eq. (1.40) of Chapter 1, it follows that the area enclosed by the orbit is $\frac{1}{2}lP$, and since the area of an ellipse is πab, we find from the previous formulas that

$$P = 2\pi \frac{a^{3/2}}{\sqrt{GM}},$$
(2.25)

which is Kepler's third law.

Case $E = 0$: If $E = 0$, then $e = 1$ and the trajectory is a parabola. This corresponds to the limiting case in which the particle falls from very far away (formally an infinite distance) and returns back there.

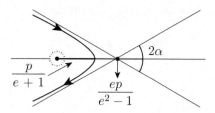

Fig. 2.5. Hyperbolic orbit.

This is the case of most comets falling towards the Sun from the Kuiper belt located beyond Pluto.

Case $E > 0$: Unbound trajectories with $E > 0$ are hyperbolas. They also satisfy (2.22), but with $e > 1$, which now implies that there is a maximum angle ϕ, and therefore, a deviation angle 2α, where $\cos(\pi - \alpha) = e^{-1}$, as shown in Fig. 2.5

Since $x = r\cos\phi$, it follows from (2.22) that $r = p - ex$, and the trajectory in Cartesian coordinates turns out to be, with some simple algebra,

$$[(e^2 - 1)x - ep]^2 - (e^2 - 1)y^2 = p^2. \tag{2.26}$$

This equation describes the two branches of a hyperbola centered around the point $x = ep/(e^2 - 1)$ and $y = 0$ (Fig. 2.5). The trajectory of the particle is the left branch of the hyperbola with the attracting center at the origin. The minimum distance to the attracting center is $p/(1 + e)$, and the deviation angle is the slope of the asymptotes $\pm\sqrt{e^2 - 1} = \pm\tan\alpha$.

This is the case of close encounters between speedy stars or the scattering of particles of opposing charges (as in Section 3.1.1).

2.2.1. *The Runge–Lenz vector*

It is clear from the above analysis that the orbital motion of a particle subject to a radial force admits four constants of motion, namely the three components of the angular momentum and the energy.

As a curiosity, we mention that for any inverse-square central force such as $\mathbf{F} = -K\mathbf{r}/r^3$, there is another constant of motion given by the Runge–Lenz vector $\mathbf{A}$, which is defined as

$$\mathbf{A} = \mathbf{v} \times \mathbf{L} - K\mathbf{r}/r. \tag{2.27}$$

It is a conserved vector because

$$d\mathbf{A}/dt = 0,$$

as can be checked using the vector formulas $\dot{r} = (\mathbf{r} \cdot \mathbf{v})/r$ and

$$\frac{d}{dt}(\mathbf{r}/r) = \frac{\mathbf{v}}{r} - \frac{(\mathbf{r} \cdot \mathbf{v})}{r^3}\mathbf{r},$$

together with the conservation of $\mathbf{L}$.[5]

At perihelion or aphelion, the vectors $\mathbf{v} \times \mathbf{L}$ and $\mathbf{r}$, and so also $\mathbf{A}$, are directed along the semi-major axis of the elliptic orbit. Thus, since the Runge–Lenz vector is conserved, it always stays parallel to the semi-major axis independent of the position of the planet.

Note also that the three components of this vector are not independent, since $\mathbf{L} \cdot \mathbf{A} = 0$ and, as can be shown with some straightforward vector algebra,

$$\mathbf{A} \cdot \mathbf{A} = K^2 + \frac{2}{m}L^2 E, \tag{2.28}$$

where

$$E = \frac{m}{2}v^2 - \frac{K}{r}$$

is the total conserved energy. Thus, there is only one additional independent constant of motion given by the Runge–Lenz vector.

2.3. Poisson equation and multipolar expansion

Until now, we have considered the gravitational field of point masses. In this section, we show how to calculate the gravitational field produced by any mass distribution. Let us first consider a point mass m enclosed in a given closed surface S, as shown in Fig. 2.6. Let r be the distance from the mass point to a point on that surface where $\mathbf{n}$ is the unit normal vector and dA is a differential element of surface

---

[5]Use also $\mathbf{a} \times (\mathbf{b} \times \mathbf{c}) = (\mathbf{a} \cdot \mathbf{c})\mathbf{b} - (\mathbf{a} \cdot \mathbf{b})\mathbf{c}$.

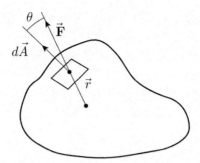

Fig. 2.6. Point mass in closed surface.

area. At that same point on the surface, the gravitational force **F** makes an angle θ with the unit vector **n**. Therefore,

$$\mathbf{F} \cdot \mathbf{n} \, dA = Gm \frac{\cos \theta}{r^2} dA = Gm \, d\Omega, \tag{2.29}$$

since $\cos \theta \, dA = r^2 \, d\Omega$, and $d\Omega$ is the element of solid angle subtended by the surface dA, as seen from the position of the point mass.

Now, an integration of $Gm \, d\Omega$ over the whole surface simply gives

$$\oint \mathbf{F} \cdot \mathbf{n} \, dA = 4\pi Gm \tag{2.30}$$

if the point mass is inside the surface; if it is outside, the integral is zero since the terms $\mathbf{F} \cdot \mathbf{n}$ will cancel each others in pairs, as can be seen from Fig. 2.6.

Summing up all the masses inside the surface, we conclude that the surface integral is related to the volume of mass inside that surface as

$$\oint \mathbf{F} \cdot \mathbf{n} \, dA = 4\pi G \int_V \rho(\mathbf{x}) dV, \tag{2.31}$$

where $\rho(\mathbf{x})$ is the enclosed mass density.

We can now use Gauss' theorem that relates a surface integral to a volume integral and get the result

$$\int_V \nabla \cdot \mathbf{F} \, dV = 4\pi G \int_V \rho(\mathbf{r}) dV, \tag{2.32}$$

and since this result must be independent of the shape of the volume, we finally find

$$\nabla^2 \Phi(\mathbf{r}) = -4\pi G \rho(\mathbf{r}) \tag{2.33}$$

in terms of the potential, $\mathbf{F} = -\nabla\Phi$. The above formula is known as Poisson's equation.[6]

It is important to note that the Poisson equation permits one to calculate the gravitational potential *inside* a given mass distribution. Outside this mass distribution, there is only vacuum and the Poisson equation reduces to the Laplace equation[7]

$$\nabla^2\Phi(\mathbf{r}) = 0, \tag{2.34}$$

which, of course, must be solved taking into account the continuity with the potential inside the massive body, or at least with its symmetry properties.

This result can be applied, for instance, to the calculation of the gravitational field produced by a mass distribution with a slight deviation from spherical symmetry. For this purpose, it is enough to note that

$$\Phi(\mathbf{r}) = -GM\left(\frac{1}{r} + \frac{\mathbf{p}\cdot\mathbf{r}}{r^3} + \cdots\right)$$

satisfies the Laplace equation if $\mathbf{p}$ is a constant vector (to prove this, recall that $\nabla r = \mathbf{r}/r$, $\nabla(\mathbf{p}\cdot\mathbf{r}) = \mathbf{p}$ and $\nabla\cdot\mathbf{r} = 3$); $\mathbf{p}$ is the *dipole* vector. If we choose the z axis along the dipole vector and use the gradient form of the divergence operator in spherical coordinates (r, θ, ϕ), we find that the gravitational force, $\mathbf{F} = -\nabla\Phi$, has components

$$F_r = -GM\left(\frac{1}{r^2} + 2p\frac{\cos\theta}{r^3}\right),$$

$$F_\theta = -GM\,p\frac{\sin\theta}{r^3}, \tag{2.35}$$

$$F_\phi = 0.$$

We see that at large distances, the leading term is the same as that of a point mass and decays as $1/r^2$, as expected. It is followed by the dipole contribution that decays as $1/r^3$. The next term, not

---

[6]After Siméon Denis Poisson (1781–1840), French mathematician.
[7]After Pierre-Simon Laplace (1749–1827), French mathematician and physicist.

considered here, is the quadrupole correction that decays as $1/r^4$, and further terms vanish even more rapidly for a larger r. In practice, it is sufficient to restrict the calculations to the dipole term and very occasionally to the quadrupole term. The motion of a particle in a dipolar field will be studied in Chapter 7.

2.4. Tidal forces

In Chapter 1, we studied the motion of bodies in a uniform gravitational field. This is a good approximation if the motion takes place in a relatively small region on the surface of the Earth (or any planet). For a large and extended mass, however, the variation of the gravitational force on different parts of the body must be taken into account since this force is not strictly uniform. Tidal forces are due to this variation: the attraction of the Sun or the Moon on the Earth, for instance, is slightly larger on one side of the Earth than on the other.

Let us consider two spherical bodies (planets or satellites), one with mass M and radius R, and the other with mass m and radius r, at a distance D between their centers; let us call the former primary and the latter secondary. On the surface of the secondary, consider a small piece of mass δm. It is attracted by the primary with a force of magnitude

$$F = \frac{GM\,\delta m}{(D-r)^2} \approx \frac{GM\,\delta m}{D^2}\left(1 + 2\frac{r}{D}\right)$$

if terms of order $(r/D)^2$ are neglected (the radius of the secondary is much smaller than its distance to the center of the primary). Thus, the mass δm, being slightly closer to the primary, is attracted by an additional force

$$2GM\,\delta m\,r/D^3,$$

which is the tidal force: it decreases as the cube of the distance to the attracting mass. On the other hand, the gravitational force exerted on δm by the secondary itself is

$$Gm\,\delta m/r^2.$$

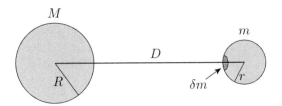

Fig. 2.7. Tidal force on δm.

If we compare the tidal force of the primary with the gravitational attraction of the secondary, both exerted in opposite directions on the piece δm (Fig. 2.7), we see that the two are of equal magnitude and compensate each other if

$$D = r(2M/m)^{1/3},$$

or, in terms of the densities ρ_M and ρ_m of the two bodies,

$$D = R \left(\frac{2\rho_M}{\rho_m} \right)^{1/3}$$

(since $M/m = \rho_M R^3/\rho_m r^3$).

This is the minimum distance at which a secondary with no internal cohesion can orbit a primary without being disrupted by its tidal forces; this would be the case, for instance, of a self-gravitating dust ball. For more realistic solid bodies with internal cohesion, such as natural or artificial satellites, the radius can be much smaller depending on their solidity. The minimum distance at which a real body can orbit a star or a planet is called the *Roche limit*.[8] It is usually believed that the rings of Saturn (and other major planets) are debris that were unable to form a satellite due to the tidal force of the giant planet.

2.5. Newtonian cosmology

The expansion of the Universe is one of the most important astronomical discoveries of modern times. Its precise description

---

[8]After Édouard Roche (1820–1883), French astronomer.

requires the general theory of relativity in full, but, as shown in the following, the most basic results can be obtained with a non-rigorous heuristic model.[9]

Imagine an infinite universe with a uniform time-dependent distribution of matter (without pressure, such as dust). Consider a spherical section of this universe with an arbitrary radius R centered on an arbitrary point O, as shown in Fig. 2.8. Now, imagine the rest of the universe as a succession of spherical shells centered on O. According to our analysis at the beginning of this chapter, these external shells do not produce any gravitational force on the sphere of radius R, which is subject to its own gravity as if its mass were concentrated at its center. Thus, the acceleration of the radius of the sphere is

$$\ddot{R} = -\frac{GM}{R^2},$$

(2.36)

where M is the mass inside the sphere,

$$M = \frac{4\pi}{3} R^3 \rho,$$

and ρ is the (time-dependent) mass density. Clearly, since $\rho \propto 1/R^3$, the mass M inside the sphere remains constant. Thus, multiplying

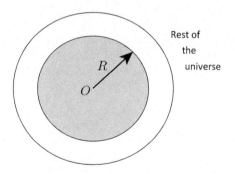

Fig. 2.8. A spherical section of a homogeneous universe.

---

[9]This non-relativistic model was originally proposed by E.A. Milne and W.H. McCrea, *Quarterly Journal of Mathematics*, **5**, 64 and 73 (1934).

by $\dot{R}$, we can easily integrate (2.36) and obtain

$$E = \frac{1}{2}\dot{R}^2 - \frac{4\pi}{3}GR^2\rho, \tag{2.37}$$

where E is a constant of integration, which can be identified as the total energy (per unit mass). In the RHS side, the first term is the kinetic energy and the second term is the gravitational potential $\propto R^{-1}$.

In all the above equations, R can be taken as the distance between two arbitrary points of the universe, say two galaxies. At the present time, R is increasing and will increase forever if $E \geq 0$; otherwise, if $E < 0$, the universe will expand, reach a maximum and then contract.

It is convenient to rewrite the above equation (2.37) as

$$\frac{1}{2}H_0^2 = \frac{E}{R^2} + \frac{4\pi}{3}GR^2\rho, \tag{2.38}$$

where H_0 is the Hubble constant,[10] defined as the present time value of $\dot{R}/R$. In our expanding universe, the distance D between two galaxies increases with a velocity $V = H_0 D$.

The value $E = 0$ is the limiting case between expansion forever and contraction at some point. The corresponding critical value of the density is

$$\rho_{crit} = \frac{3H_0^2}{8\pi G},$$

as it follows from (2.38).

Of course, this is a toy model, but some of the results remain valid with a rigorous relativist treatment (which is beyond our present purpose).

---

[10] Edwinn Hubble (1889–1953), American astronomer who discovered the expansion of the Universe.

Chapter 3

Scattering and Systems of Particles

Ernest Rutherford (1871–1937) deduced the structure of the atom with a classical experiment performed in 1909 by his collaborators Hans Geiger (1882–1945) and Ernest Marsden (1889–1970). They fired alpha particles (nuclei of helium, as we now know) to a thin sheet of gold and noted that most of them were not deflected from their initial trajectories, but a few suffered a strong scattering. This effect can only be explained if the alpha particles are scattered by an almost point-like charge, in this case, the nuclei of gold atoms.

Let us analyze the trajectory of a charged particle deviated by another charged particle due to a central force, which can be attractive or repulsive.

3.1. Rutherford scattering

The potential energy of a particle with mass m and charge q due to the Coulomb attraction or repulsion of a charge Q located at the origin of coordinates is

$$m\ddot{\mathbf{r}} = \frac{K}{r^3}\mathbf{r}, \tag{3.1}$$

where $K = qQ$ (in Gaussian units) and $K > 0$ (<0) for a repulsive (attractive) force. Since a nucleus of gold is about 20 times heavier than an alpha particle, it is a good approximation to take the nucleus as fixed. (Otherwise, one can use the formalism of the following sections.)

We can follow exactly the same procedure used in the Kepler problem. The result, corresponding to Eq. (2.22) of Chapter 2, is

$$r = \frac{p}{e\cos\phi - 1},\tag{3.2}$$

where

$$p = \frac{L^2}{mK}$$

and the eccentricity is given by

$$e = \sqrt{1 + 2EL^2/(mK^2)}\tag{3.3}$$

in analogy with Eq. (2.23) of Chapter 2. E and L are the energy and angular momentum of the impinging particle.

Clearly, there are no bound orbits for a repulsive force; thus, E is always positive and $e > 1$. The trajectory is an hyperbola bounded between the asymptotes at angles $\pm\alpha$, where $\cos\alpha = e^{-1}$ (see Fig. 3.1). The deflection angle of the particle is 2α and the minimum distance it can approach to the origin is $p/(e - 1)$. In Cartesian coordinates, the trajectory is again given by (2.26), but now it is the right branch of a hyperbola, as seen in Fig. 2.5 of Chapter 2.

Suppose the impinging particle is fired from far away along a straight line such that, if no repulsion were present, it would go past

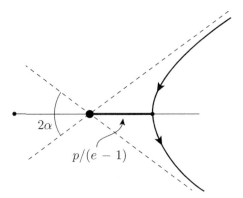

Fig. 3.1.   Trajectory in a repulsive potential.

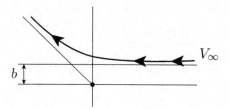

Fig. 3.2. Scattering parameters.

the repelling center at a distance b. This parameter is the *impact parameter*, as seen in Fig. 3.2. Since E and L are constants of motion, their values can be calculated at their initial positions, from where they were shot. Thus,

$$E = \frac{1}{2}mv_\infty^2,$$

$$L = mbv_\infty,$$

where v_∞ is the initial velocity of the impinging particle. Now, the scattering angle is $\theta = \pi - 2\alpha$, as shown in Fig. 3.2; then, with a little trigonometry and algebra,

$$\tan(\theta/2) = \cot\alpha = \frac{1}{\sqrt{e^2 - 1}}$$

$$= \sqrt{\frac{mK^2}{2EL^2}} = \frac{K}{mbv_\infty^2},$$

and therefore,

$$b = \frac{K}{mv_\infty^2}\cot(\theta/2). \tag{3.4}$$

Consider now the following problem: A bunch of N particles is fired from an infinite distance directly to the repelling center. Question: How many dN of these particles will be deflected between angles θ and $\theta + d\theta$? From Fig. 3.3 and the axial symmetry of the problem, we see that

$$dN = N\,d\sigma,$$

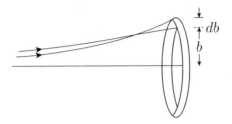

Fig. 3.3. Scattering of a bunch of particles.

where

$$d\sigma = 2\pi b \, db \tag{3.5}$$

is the area of a ring of radius b and width db.

It then follows with a little algebra that

$$d\sigma = \left(\frac{K}{2mv_\infty^2}\right)^2 \frac{d\Omega}{\sin^4(\theta/2)}, \tag{3.6}$$

where $d\Omega = 2\pi \sin\theta \, d\theta$ is the differential of solid angle (for a ring of angular width $d\theta$). This is Rutherford's scattering formula. It gives the fraction of particles scattered as a function of the scattering angle. Most of the particles go past with very little dispersion, but a few of them are dispersed at various directions at large angles.

The quantity σ is an important parameter called *scattering cross-section*. It has dimensions of area and is a measure of the strength and size of a scattering object, such as an atomic nucleus. In nuclear physics, σ is usually measured in *barns*; one barn is 10^{-28} m^2, and the typical length scale of a nucleus is the femtometre or fermi, 10^{-15} m.

3.1.1. *Attractive potential*

A similar analysis applies to the problem of attractive forces, such as the scattering of a fast electron by a (positively charged) ion or the unbound motion in a close encounter of two massive bodies, say, the Earth and a comet or an asteroid. Again, we assume that one of the bodies is massive enough to remain at rest and the other is coming from an infinite distance with an initial velocity v_∞ and an impact parameter b. The treatment is exactly the same as in the

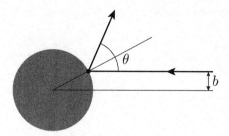

Fig. 3.4. Scattering by a hard sphere.

previous section, and the above formulas apply also with negative K. The only difference is that the impact parameter must be taken as negative, but this does not change the resulting cross-section.

3.1.2. *Scattering by a hard sphere*

As a very simple example, let us apply a similar procedure to the elastic scattering of a point particle from a rigid and fixed sphere of radius a (see Fig. 3.4). Since the scattering is totally elastic, a particle impinging with an impact parameter b will be reflected at an angle θ such that

$$b = a \sin \frac{\pi - \theta}{2} = a \cos \frac{\theta}{2}, \qquad (3.7)$$

as can be seen from Fig. 3.4 with some simple trigonometry. Using formula (3.5), we find

$$d\sigma = \frac{\pi}{2} a^2 \sin \theta \, d\theta. \qquad (3.8)$$

Note that this differential cross-section can be integrated over all angles, $0 \leq \theta < \pi$, yielding the total cross-section

$$\sigma = \pi a^2,$$

which simply means that the impinging particles "see" a scattering surface πa^2. This is the obvious meaning of the scattering cross-section defined above: the bigger the σ, the stronger the deflecting interaction.

3.2. System of particles

The previous chapters were devoted to the motion of a single particle. We now study the case of a system of two or more particles, such that each particle has a mass m_n and is located at a position $\mathbf{r_n}$, with velocity $\mathbf{v_n}$. It is convenient to define the *center of mass* $\mathbf{R}$ as

$$\mathbf{R} \equiv \frac{\sum_n m_n \mathbf{r_n}}{\sum_n m_n} \tag{3.9}$$

and the total momentum as

$$\mathbf{P} \equiv \sum_n m_n \mathbf{v_n}, \tag{3.10}$$

with the total mass of the system being $M = \sum_n m_n$. Therefore, according to (3.9),

$$\mathbf{P} = M\dot{\mathbf{R}}. \tag{3.11}$$

In the continuum limit, the sum must be replaced by an integral:

$$\mathbf{R} = \frac{\int \mathbf{r}\rho(\mathbf{r})dV}{\int \rho(\mathbf{r})dV} = \frac{\int \mathbf{r}\rho(\mathbf{r})dV}{M}, \tag{3.12}$$

where $\rho(\mathbf{r})$ is the mass density, with a similar expression for $\mathbf{P}$.

The time derivative of $\mathbf{P}$ is the sum of all the forces $\mathbf{F_n}$ acting on each particle. These forces have two components, one due to external forces, $\mathbf{F_n^{ext}}$, and another due to the mutual interactions between all the particles. By Newton's third law, the mutual forces, summed over all pairs of particles, cancel each other. Thus, the acceleration of the center of mass is due entirely to the external forces acting on the system, that is,

$$M\ddot{\mathbf{R}} = \sum_n \mathbf{F_n^{ext}} \equiv \mathbf{F}.$$

An important consequence of this result is that, in the absence of external forces, the velocity of the center of mass is constant: it is therefore always possible to choose an *inertial* reference frame in which the center of mass of the whole system is at rest. In such reference frame, $\dot{\mathbf{R}} = 0$ and the total momentum is zero according to (3.11):

$$\mathbf{P} = 0.$$

This defines the *center of momentum frame*.

As for the angular momentum of a system of particles, for each particle, we have

$$\mathbf{L_n} = m_n \mathbf{r_n} \times \dot{\mathbf{r}}_\mathbf{n},$$

and therefore,

$$\frac{d}{dt}\mathbf{L_n} = m_n \mathbf{r_n} \times \ddot{\mathbf{r}}_\mathbf{n} = \mathbf{r_n} \times \mathbf{F_n}.$$

Again, the mutual interactions between the particles make no contributions. To see this, consider two particles of the system, say, particles 1 and 2, such that the interaction forces between them are $\pm\mathbf{F_{12}}$. Therefore, their contribution to the angular momentum is

$$\mathbf{r_1} \times \mathbf{F_{12}} - \mathbf{r_2} \times \mathbf{F_{12}} = (\mathbf{r_1} - \mathbf{r_2}) \times \mathbf{F_{12}}.$$

But $(\mathbf{r_1} - \mathbf{r_2})$ is the vector uniting the two particles, and it is usually parallel to $\mathbf{F_{12}}$, as, for instance, in the important case of the gravitational attraction between the particles. Thus, the above sum is zero. The same argument applies to all pairs of particles in the system, and we can conclude that only external forces must be taken into account, namely

$$\frac{d}{dt}\mathbf{L} = \sum_n \mathbf{r_n} \times \mathbf{F_n^{ext}} \equiv \mathbf{K},$$

where $\mathbf{L} \equiv \sum_n \mathbf{L_n}$ is the total angular momentum and $\mathbf{K}$ is defined as the *total torque* acting on the system *from outside*.

3.2.1. *The two-bodies problem*

Consider the general case of two mutually interacting particles scattered by a close encounter between them. Suppose that the scattering is perfectly *elastic* in the sense that there is no loss of internal energy in the form of thermal energy or deformation of

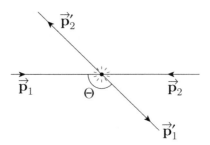

Fig. 3.5. Scattering in the center of momentum.

the particles: there is only an interchange of kinetic energy and momentum between the particles.

According to the discussion in the previous section, it is possible, in the absence of external forces, to choose an inertial reference frame in which the center of mass is at rest and the total momentum is zero. In this center of momentum (CM) frame, the momenta of the two particles must be $\mathbf{p}_{CM}$ and $-\mathbf{p}_{CM}$, since the sum of momenta must be zero by the very definition of CM. Again, due to the conservation of total momentum, the momenta must be $\mathbf{p}'_{CM}$ and $-\mathbf{p}'_{CM}$ after the scattering, as shown in Fig. 3.5. Accordingly, there is a single parameter, the angle Θ, which defines the scattering directions of the two particles.

Furthermore, the kinetic energy in the CM frame is

$$E_{CM} = \frac{|\mathbf{p}_{CM}|^2}{m_1} + \frac{|\mathbf{p}_{CM}|^2}{m_2} = \frac{|\mathbf{p}_{CM}|^2}{\mu}, \tag{3.13}$$

where

$$\mu = \frac{m_1 m_2}{m_1 + m_2} \tag{3.14}$$

(or $\mu^{-1} = m_1^{-1} + m_2^{-1}$) is the *reduced mass* of the two particles. The conservation of total energy implies that $|\mathbf{p}_{CM}| = |\mathbf{p}'_{CM}|$, and thus, $\mathbf{p}_{CM} \cdot \mathbf{p}'_{CM} = |\mathbf{p}_{CM}|^2 \cos \Theta$.

Clearly, the process takes its simplest form in the CM frame. In a laboratory frame, which can be *any* inertial frame, the particles have velocities $\mathbf{v}_1$ and $\mathbf{v}_2$, and momenta $m_1 \mathbf{v}_1$ and $m_2 \mathbf{v}_2$. The velocity $\mathbf{v}_0$

of the CM system in the laboratory frame is

$$\mathbf{v}_0 = \frac{m_1 \mathbf{v}_1 + m_2 \mathbf{v}_2}{m_1 + m_2}, \tag{3.15}$$

and the momenta are

$$\mathbf{p}_1 = \mathbf{p}_{CM} + m_1 \mathbf{v}_0,$$
$$\mathbf{p}_2 = -\mathbf{p}_{CM} + m_2 \mathbf{v}_0, \tag{3.16}$$

from where it follows that

$$\mathbf{p}_1 + \mathbf{p}_2 = (m_1 + m_2)\mathbf{v}_0, \quad \mathbf{p}_{CM} = \mu(\mathbf{v}_1 - \mathbf{v}_2). \tag{3.17}$$

After the scattering, the new momenta are

$$\mathbf{p}_1' = \mathbf{p}_{CM}' + m_1 \mathbf{v}_0,$$
$$\mathbf{p}_2' = -\mathbf{p}_{CM}' + m_2 \mathbf{v}_0, \tag{3.18}$$

or

$$\mathbf{p}_1' = \mathbf{p}_{CM}' + \frac{m_1}{m_1 + m_2}(\mathbf{p}_1 + \mathbf{p}_2),$$

$$\mathbf{p}_2' = -\mathbf{p}_{CM}' + \frac{m_2}{m_1 + m_2}(\mathbf{p}_1 + \mathbf{p}_2). \tag{3.19}$$

In general, the relation between the scattering angles as measured in the laboratory and in the CM frames can be calculated, but the result is not very illustrating. However, the particular case of one of the particles being initially at rest is relatively simple to handle. Suppose, then, that particle 2 is at rest, and therefore, $\mathbf{v}_2 = 0$ and $\mathbf{p}_{CM} = \mu\mathbf{v}_1$. Setting $\mathbf{p}_2 = 0$ in (3.19), it follows with some straightforward algebra that

$$(p_1')^2 = \frac{m_1^2 + m_2^2 + 2m_1 m_2 \cos\Theta}{(m_1 + m_2)^2} p_1^2,$$

$$(p_2')^2 = \frac{2m_2^2}{(m_1 + m_2)^2}(1 - \cos\Theta)p_1^2, \tag{3.20}$$

and $(p_2')^2/2m_2$ is the energy lost by the impinging particle and gained by particle 2 which was initially at rest. Of course, by the conservation of energy,

$$\frac{(p'_1)^2}{2m_1} + \frac{(p'_2)^2}{2m_2} = \frac{p_1^2}{2m_1},$$

as easily checked.

It also follows from (3.19) (with $\mathbf{p}_2 = 0$) that

$$\mathbf{v}_1 \cdot \mathbf{v}'_1 = \frac{v_1^2}{m_1 + m_2}(m_1 + m_2 \cos \Theta),$$

$$\mathbf{v}_1 \cdot \mathbf{v}'_2 = \frac{v_1^2 m_1}{m_1 + m_2}(1 - \cos \Theta),$$

relating the scattering angles of the two particles with the corresponding angle Θ in the CM frame. Explicitly, using the values of the velocities taken from (3.20), we find with some straightforward algebra and trigonometry

$$\tan \theta_1 = \frac{m_2 \sin \Theta}{m_1 + m_2 \cos \Theta}, \qquad \theta_2 = \frac{\pi - \Theta}{2}, \qquad (3.21)$$

where θ_1 and θ_2 are the scattering angles with respect to the direction of the impinging particle in the laboratory frame.

This is as far as one can get with purely kinematic arguments. The scattering angle must be determined by the explicit form of the interaction between the two particles.

3.2.2. *Interacting pair of particles*

In the previous chapter, we studied the motion of a celestial body, assuming that the mass of the attracting body is much larger than that of the moving body (for instance, the Sun attracting a planet), and we thus supposed that the former is fixed at the origin of coordinates. In a more realistic situation, the finite masses of the two bodies must be taken into account.

In accordance with the concept of center of mass, consider the general case of a force (not necessarily gravitational) between two particles that depends only on the separation between them. If $\mathbf{r}_1$ and $\mathbf{r}_2$ are the position vectors of the two particles, with masses m_1 and m_2, and the force between them is such that it is along the direction $\mathbf{r}_1 - \mathbf{r}_2$, then according to Newton's second and third laws of motion,

$$m_1\ddot{\mathbf{r}}_1 = F(|\mathbf{r}_1 - \mathbf{r}_2|)(\mathbf{r}_2 - \mathbf{r}_1),$$
$$m_2\ddot{\mathbf{r}}_2 = F(|\mathbf{r}_1 - \mathbf{r}_2|)(\mathbf{r}_1 - \mathbf{r}_2), \tag{3.22}$$

if no external forces are present.

Define the vectors

$$\mathbf{r} = \mathbf{r}_2 - \mathbf{r}_1, \tag{3.23}$$

and the center of mass of the system given by

$$\mathbf{R} = \frac{m_1\mathbf{r}_1 + m_2\mathbf{r}_2}{m_1 + m_2}. \tag{3.24}$$

Following the discussion of the last section, the velocity of the center of mass can be taken as $\mathbf{R} = \mathbf{0}$ without loss of generality. Thus,

$$\mathbf{r}_1 = -\frac{m_2}{m}\mathbf{r}, \quad \mathbf{r}_2 = \frac{m_1}{m}\mathbf{r}, \tag{3.25}$$

where $m = m_1 + m_2$ is the total mass, and it follows from the equations in (3.22) that

$$\mu\ddot{\mathbf{r}} = F(r)\mathbf{r}, \tag{3.26}$$

where μ is the reduced mass of the system (3.14).

As mentioned above, the momenta of the particles in the center of mass system are of the same magnitude and opposite sign. This common momentum is

$$\mathbf{p}_{\text{CM}} = \mu\dot{\mathbf{r}}, \tag{3.27}$$

and the momentum of each particle is $\mathbf{p}_{\text{CM}}$ and $-\mathbf{p}_{\text{CM}}$.

Note also that the total kinetic energy T and angular momentum of the two particles are

$$T = \frac{1}{2}m_1\dot{\mathbf{r}}_1^2 + \frac{1}{2}m_2\dot{\mathbf{r}}_2^2 = \frac{1}{2}\mu\dot{\mathbf{r}}^2, \tag{3.28}$$
$$\mathbf{L} = m_1\mathbf{r}_1 \times \dot{\mathbf{r}}_1 + m_2\mathbf{r}_2 \times \dot{\mathbf{r}}_2 = \mu\mathbf{r} \times \dot{\mathbf{r}}, \tag{3.29}$$

and the total energy is

$$E = \frac{1}{2}\mu\dot{\mathbf{r}}^2 + \frac{L^2}{2\mu r^2} + U(r). \tag{3.30}$$

Thus, the two-bodies problem has been reduced to a one-body problem. It is enough to change the mass of the single particle in the one-body problem to the effective mass μ (given by Eq. (3.26)) and take the radial distance as $\mathbf{r} = \mathbf{r}_2 - \mathbf{r}_1$.

3.2.3. *Gravitating binary system*

Let us apply the above procedure to the particular case of two gravitating bodies. The equations of motion (in the CM) frame reduce to the form

$$\ddot{\mathbf{r}} = -\frac{Gm}{r^3}\mathbf{r} \tag{3.31}$$

with a potential

$$U(r) = -\frac{Gm\mu}{r}$$

(recall $m = m_1 + m_2$). From what we already know about the one-body problem, we can deduce that each particle (star, planet or satellite) follows an elliptic trajectory, as shown in Fig. 3.6: their positions are given by equations in (3.22). Both particles orbit their common center of mass along ellipses, always opposing each other. As expected, the more massive body moves in a smaller orbit (Fig. 3.7).

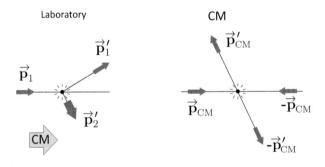

Fig. 3.6.   Scattering as seen in the laboratory and in the CM frames.

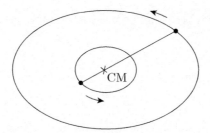

Fig. 3.7. Gravitating binary system.

3.2.4. *Ion–ion scattering*

Consider now the scattering of two charged particles with different masses but charges of equal sign, for instance, two ions or two electrons (without considering, of course, quantum effects at this level). We can still take one of the particles initially at rest in the laboratory frame and the other impinging from an infinite distance, but the recoil of the former after the scattering must be taken into account. For this reason, it is convenient to work in the center of momentum (CM) frame and then return to the laboratory frame.

As we have seen in the previous section, the equations of motion for two interacting particles, without external forces, are the same as for one particle with the mass replaced by the reduced mass. Accordingly, in the CM frame, the total energy is

$$E = \frac{1}{2}\mu\dot{\mathbf{r}}^2 + \frac{L^2}{2\mu r^2} + \frac{K}{r}, \qquad (3.32)$$

with $L = \mu r^2 \dot{\phi}$ and $E = (1/2)\mu v_\infty^2$ as in the Rutherford scattering treated in Section 3.1 (recall that v_∞ is the initial *relative* velocity between the two particles and it is the same in the laboratory and in the CM frames). Thus, all we have to do is to substitute μ for m in the previously obtained formula (3.6)

$$d\sigma = 2\pi \left(\frac{K}{2\mu v_\infty^2}\right)^2 \frac{\sin\Theta\,d\Theta}{\sin^4(\Theta/2)}, \qquad (3.33)$$

taking into account that Θ is the scattering angle in the CM frame. To return to the laboratory frame, we must use the relations (3.21) for the scattering angles. For the motion of particle 2 (the one initially at rest), we find

$$d\sigma = 4\pi \left(\frac{K}{2\mu v_\infty^2} \right)^2 \frac{\sin\theta_2 \, d\theta_2}{\cos^3\theta_2}, \tag{3.34}$$

since $\Theta = \pi - 2\theta_2$. For the impinging particle, the relation between the two angles is quite cumbersome and will not be worked out here. In any case, if the two particles have the same mass m, then $2\theta_1 = \Theta$ according to (3.21), and so, all we have to do is to substitute this value of Θ in (3.33) with $\mu = m/2$.

Chapter 4

Non-Inertial Frames

Until now, we considered fixed reference frames without inertial forces. In this chapter, we study the motion in a rotating frame in which there are inertial forces that must be taken into account. Consider then a two-dimensional Cartesian coordinate system, (x', y') rotating around the origin of a fixed system (x, y) with angular velocity Ω, as shown in Fig. 4.1. The relation between the two systems of coordinates is given by the formula

$$
\begin{aligned}
x' &= \cos(\Omega t)x + \sin(\Omega t)y, \\
y' &= -\sin(\Omega t)x + \cos(\Omega t)y.
\end{aligned}
\tag{4.1}
$$

After deriving twice these equations with respect of time, it easily follows that the acceleration in the rotating frame is

$$
\ddot{\mathbf{r}}' = \ddot{\mathbf{r}}_{\text{fixed}} - 2\boldsymbol{\Omega} \times \dot{\mathbf{r}}' + \boldsymbol{\Omega} \times (\boldsymbol{\Omega} \times \mathbf{r}'),
\tag{4.2}
$$

where $\mathbf{r}_{\text{fixed}} = (x, y)$ refers to the fixed frame and $\mathbf{r}' = (x', y')$ to the rotating frame. The angular velocity vector $\boldsymbol{\Omega}$ is perpendicular to the plane of rotation, i.e., in the $z = z'$ direction. Clearly, the first term on the right-hand side of this equation is the acceleration due to the force acting in the inertial frame. The second term, which is proportional to the angular velocity Ω, is the Coriolis force[1]; it is perpendicular to the velocity, and thus, it performs no work (as is also the case

---

[1]Named after Gaspard-Gustave de Coriolis (1792–1843), French mathematician and engineer.

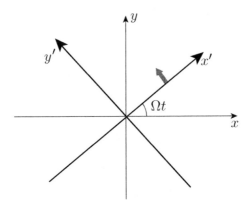

Fig. 4.1. Fixed and rotating frames.

of a magnetic field acting on a charged particle). The last term, proportional to Ω^2, is the centrifugal acceleration force, which is perpendicular to the rotation axis. In order to analyze these terms in more detail, let us study two problems: the effect of the Coriolis force on the surface of the Earth and the restricted problem of gravitating three bodies.

4.1. Coriolis force

The Coriolis force on the surface of the Earth is due to its rotation. Its effects are rather negligible at small scales, but can be observed with the Foucault pendulum.[2] However, at a very large scale, it is responsible for the formation of hurricanes. Let us analyze the two cases.

4.1.1. *Foucault pendulum*

Consider a long pendulum oscillating above the horizontal (x, y) plane. If the amplitude of the oscillation is small enough (Fig. 4.2), the vertical motion can be neglected and we consider only the projection of the motion on the (x, y) plane. The last term in (4.2), which is due to the centripetal acceleration, is negligible in

---

[2]Léon Foucault (1819–1868), French physicist.

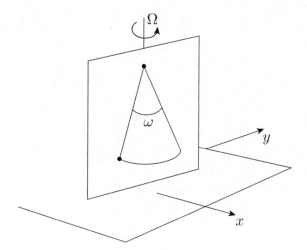

Fig. 4.2. Foucault's pendulum.

comparison with the Coriolis force, as can be checked by a simple numerical evaluation. Accordingly, from (4.2), the motion of the pendulum is well described by the equations

$$\ddot{x} + \omega^2 x = 2\Omega \dot{y},$$
$$\ddot{y} + \omega^2 y = -2\Omega \dot{x},$$
(4.3)

where $\omega = \sqrt{g/L}$ is the natural frequency of oscillation of the pendulum and Ω is the angular velocity of the rotating Earth at the position of the pendulum.

If Ω_0 is the overall angular velocity of the Earth $(2\pi/24$ hours) and λ is the latitude measured from the Equator (see Fig. 4.3), then

$$\Omega = \Omega_0 \sin \lambda.$$

For the southern hemisphere, $\lambda < 0$.

To solve the above pair of equations, we define a complex coordinate $Z = x + iy$ that reduces them to

$$\ddot{Z} + 2i\Omega \dot{Z} + \omega^2 Z = 0,$$
(4.4)

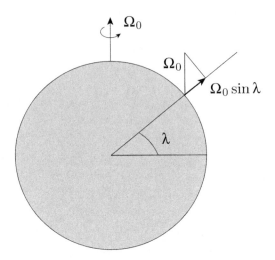

Fig. 4.3. Projection of the Earth's angular momentum.

with a simple solution

$$Z = e^{-i\alpha t} Z_0,$$

where Z_0 is a constant and $\alpha \approx \pm\omega + \Omega$ (note that in all practical cases, $\Omega \ll \omega$). Thus,

$$Z = e^{-i\Omega t}(A_1 e^{i\omega t} + A_2 e^{-i\omega t}),$$

where A_i are constants. The term in brackets corresponds to the usual oscillations of the pendulum with frequency ω, for instance, if $A_1 = A_2 = A/2$, the unperturbed motion is along the x axis: $x = A\cos\omega t$. Additionally, however, the plane of oscillation rotates around the vertical axis with an angular velocity $\Omega = \Omega_0 \sin\lambda$.

Accordingly, the vertical plane of oscillation of the pendulum rotates making a full circle with a period $(24/\sin\lambda)$ hours due to the Coriolis force. This period depends on the latitude as $1/\sin\lambda$: it is the shortest at the poles (24 hours), and there is no rotation (infinite period time) at the Equator. Thus, for instance, the swinging plane makes a full 2π rotation in 31.8 hours at Paris, in 38 hours at Washington D.C., in 72.7 hours at Mexico City, etc.

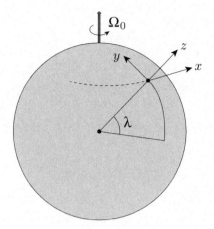

Fig. 4.4. Local system of coordinates.

4.1.2. *Free shots and hurricanes*

Let us now study the influence of the Coriolis force on a projectile fired with some initial velocity from a given point on the Earth's surface with latitude λ. As shown in Fig. 4.4, we choose the z axis perpendicular to the surface of the Earth, and the x and y axes parallel to the Equator and the meridian, respectively (see also Fig. 4.3). At latitude λ, the components of $\boldsymbol{\Omega}$ are

$$\Omega_x = 0, \quad \Omega_y = \Omega \cos \lambda, \quad \Omega_z = \Omega \sin \lambda$$

and the equations of motion, according to (4.2), are

$$\dot{v}_x = 2(-\Omega_y v_z + \Omega_z v_y),$$
$$\dot{v}_y = -2\Omega_z v_x, \tag{4.5}$$
$$\dot{v}_z = -g + 2\Omega_y v_x,$$

again neglecting the centrifugal force which is of order Ω^2. In a zeroth-order approximation, with $\boldsymbol{\Omega} = 0$, the solutions of the above equations are simply

$$v_x = v_{0x}, \quad v_y = v_{0y}, \quad v_z = v_{0z} - gt \tag{4.6}$$

(in obvious notation) and

$$x = v_{0x}t, \quad y = v_{0y}t, \quad z = v_{0z}t - \frac{1}{2}gt^2, \qquad (4.7)$$

taking the emission point of the particle at the origin of coordinates and at ground.

The angular momentum along the z axis is $L_z = xv_y - yv_x$, and its time derivative is

$$\dot{L}_z = x\dot{v}_y - y\dot{v}_x.$$

Thus, substituting the above equations of motion (4.5) and using the zeroth-order values given by (4.6) and (4.7), we find that

$$\dot{L}_z = -2\Omega_z v_{0\perp}^2 t + 2\Omega_y v_{0y} v_{0z} t \qquad (4.8)$$

$(v_\perp^2 = v_{0x}^2 + v_{0y}^2)$, and therefore,

$$L_z = -\Omega_z v_{0\perp}^2 t^2 + \Omega_y v_{0y} v_{0z} t^2 \qquad (4.9)$$

(initial condition: $L_z = 0$ at $t = 0$).

Now, we know that $L_z = r^2 \dot{\phi}$ and also $r = v_\perp t$ in the zeroth-order approximation. Then, $L_z = v_\perp^2 t^2 \dot{\phi}$, and comparing with (4.9) and integrating once, we obtain

$$v_{0\perp}^2 (\phi - \phi_0) = (-\Omega_z v_{0\perp}^2 + \Omega_y v_{0y} v_{0z}) t.$$

For a horizontal shot $(v_{0y} = 0)$, the above formula reduces to

$$\Delta\phi \equiv \phi - \phi_0 = -\Omega t \sin \lambda,$$

from where we deduce that the deviation is clockwise (to the right of the trajectory) in the northern hemisphere ($\lambda > 0$) and counterclockwise (to the left of the trajectory) in the southern hemisphere ($\lambda < 0$).

Hurricanes are produced when there is a region of low pressure in the atmosphere that attracts masses of air in radial direction. In the northern hemisphere, the Coriolis force deviates these masses to the right of their motion and thus produces a counterclockwise rotation (see Fig. 4.5). By the same argument, the resulting rotation is clockwise in the southern hemisphere.

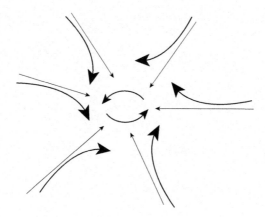

Fig. 4.5. Formation of hurricane.

4.2. The restricted three-bodies problem

As we have seen, the problem of two moving masses bound by their mutual gravitational attraction can be solved analytically without much trouble. The problem gets considerably more difficult for the motion of three or more attractive masses; such a problem defied the mathematical skills of nineteenth century physicists and it is only after the pioneering work of the great mathematician Henri Poincaré (1854–1912) that the difficulties became clear: for three or more masses, the motion may be *chaotic*, in the sense that it depends so strongly on initial conditions that it is impossible to predict the evolution of a physical system beyond a relatively short time.

Nevertheless, the restricted three-bodies problem, in which one of the masses is small enough not to affect the motion of the other two, can be studied analytically. It correctly describes the motion of a satellite in orbits around the Earth–Moon system or an asteroid in the field of the Sun–Jupiter system.

As we shall see in the following, it is convenient to work in a rotating system in which the two massive bodies, circling one another in circular orbits, appear to be at rest. Clearly, such a rotating system is not inertial and both Coriolis and centrifugal forces must be taken into account.

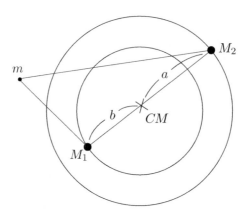

Fig. 4.6. Restricted three-bodies system.

Based on the previous analysis of rotating frames, we consider the problem of two massive bodies, with masses M_1 and M_2, rotating around their common center of mass with an angular frequency ω, as in Fig. 4.6. Assuming for simplicity that the orbits are circular, let a and b be the distances between the center of mass and M_2 and M_1, respectively, and $l = a + b$. Equating gravitational and centrifugal forces, we have $GM_1/l^2 = a\omega^2$ and $GM_2/l^2 = b\omega^2$, and therefore,

$$a = lM_1/M, \quad b = lM_2/M,$$

where $M = M_1 + M_2$ is the total mass and $\omega^2 = GM/l^3$.

Consider now a third particle of mass $m \ll M$ moving in the gravitational field of the two masses M_1 and M_2 without affecting their motion. In the fixed reference frame (called *sidereal* frame by astronomers), the position (x, y) of this particle, assumed to be in the plane perpendicular to the rotation axis, follows from the equations of motion:

$$\frac{d^2x}{dt^2} = -\frac{\partial}{\partial x}U,$$

$$\frac{d^2y}{dt^2} = -\frac{\partial}{\partial y}U,$$

(4.10)

where

$$U = -\frac{GM_1}{r_1} - \frac{GM_2}{r_2},$$

with

$$r_1 = \sqrt{(x - x_1)^2 + (y - y_1)^2},$$
$$r_2 = \sqrt{(x - x_2)^2 + (y - y_2)^2},$$

(4.11)

and where

$$x_1 = b \cos \omega t, \quad y_1 = b \sin \omega t,$$
$$x_2 = -a \cos \omega t, \quad y_2 = -a \sin \omega t$$

(4.12)

are the positions (x_i, y_i) of the two massive rotating bodies.

Summing up, the equations of motion in the sidereal reference frame are

$$\frac{d^2 x}{dt^2} = -\left[\frac{M_1(x - b \cos \omega t)}{r_1^3} + \frac{M_2(x + a \cos \omega t)}{r_2^3} \right]$$
$$\frac{d^2 y}{dt^2} = -\left[\frac{M_1(y - b \sin \omega t)}{r_1^3} + \frac{M_2(y + a \sin \omega t)}{r_2^3} \right].$$

(4.13)

We can transform to the rotating frame (X, Y) (called *synodic* frame by astronomers) with the transformation

$$X = x \cos(\omega t) + y \sin(\omega t),$$
$$Y = -x \sin(\omega t) + y \cos(\omega t).$$

(4.14)

In this frame,

$$r_1 = \sqrt{(X - b)^2 + Y^2},$$
$$r_2 = \sqrt{(X + a)^2 + Y^2},$$

(4.15)

and after some straightforward algebra, the equations of motion take the form

$$\frac{d^2 X}{dt^2} - 2\omega \frac{dY}{dt} = \frac{\partial}{\partial X} F(X, Y),$$
$$\frac{d^2 Y}{dt^2} + 2\omega \frac{dX}{dt} = \frac{\partial}{\partial Y} F(X, Y),$$

(4.16)

where

$$F(X, Y) = \frac{\omega^2}{2}(X^2 + Y^2) + G\left(\frac{M_1}{r_1} + \frac{M_2}{r_2} \right).$$

(4.17)

In the rest of this section, we will closely follow the treatment and notation given by Szebehely in his book on the restricted three-bodies problem, *Theory of Orbits*,[3] to which the reader is referred for all the details. Here, we present the most general results.

First of all, it is convenient at this point to simplify the above equations using dimensionless coordinates. Taking l, ω^{-1} and M as the units of length, time and mass, respectively, we define

$$X = l\bar{x}, \quad Y = l\bar{y}, \quad \bar{r}_i = lr_i$$

and $\omega t = \bar{t}$, where the barred variables are dimensionless. Thus, after dropping all the bars without risk of confusion (or, alternatively, simply setting l, ω and M equal to unity), Eqs. (4.16) take the form

$$\ddot{x} - 2\dot{y} = \frac{\partial}{\partial x}\Omega,$$
$$\ddot{y} + 2\dot{x} = \frac{\partial}{\partial y}\Omega, \tag{4.18}$$

where we have redefined the potential $F(X, Y)$ in the dimensionless form

$$\Omega = \frac{1}{2}(x^2 + y^2) + \frac{\mu_1}{r_1} + \frac{\mu_2}{r_2} + \frac{1}{2}\mu_1\mu_2, \tag{4.19}$$

with $\mu_i = M_i/M$ (note that $\mu_1 + \mu_2 = 1$) and

$$r_1^2 = (x - \mu_2)^2 + y^2,$$
$$r_2^2 = (x + \mu_1)^2 + y^2. \tag{4.20}$$

The function Ω, with the sign inverted (just for convenience), is the dimensionless potential with the centrifugal term included. The last term in (4.19), $\frac{1}{2}\mu_1\mu_2$, is a constant and can be dropped out of the equations of motion. An equivalent expression for Ω is

$$\Omega = \frac{1}{2}[\mu_1 r_1^2 + \mu_2 r_2^2] + \frac{\mu_1}{r_1} + \frac{\mu_2}{r_2}, \tag{4.21}$$

as it can be checked by simple algebra.

---

[3]V. Szebehely, *Theory of Orbits*, Academic Press, 1967.

Equations (4.18) with (4.21) are the basic equations of motion for the restricted three-body problem. Multiplying these two equations by $\dot{x}$ and $\dot{y}$, respectively, and summing, we obtain a first integral

$$\dot{x}^2 + \dot{y}^2 = 2\,\Omega(x, y) - C, \tag{4.22}$$

where C is an integration constant. It is (minus) the total conserved energy of the small third particle.

The motion of the small particle can be qualitatively described noting that, for a given constant C, it must be restricted inside the region $2\,\Omega = C$. Furthermore, the velocity of the particle must be zero at all the points (x, y) where this condition ($2\,\Omega = C$) is satisfied; the set of such points define a *zero-velocity* curve.

Let us analyze the form of the function Ω. Note, first, that Ω on the x axis is

$$\Omega(x, 0) = \frac{1}{2}x^2 + \frac{1}{2}\mu(1 - \mu) + \frac{1 - \mu}{r_1} + \frac{\mu}{r_2}$$

(we take $\mu_2 = \mu$ and $\mu_1 = 1 - \mu$). Clearly, $\Omega(x, 0) \to \infty$ if $r_i \to 0$. Note also that $\Omega(x, 0)$ has three minima on the x axis where $\frac{d}{dx}\Omega(x, 0) = 0$, corresponding to three *unstable* equilibrium points since $\frac{d^2}{dx^2}\Omega(x, 0) > 0$ at these points (recall that Ω is *minus* the potential energy).

These three points are called Lagrange[4] points, L_1, L_2 and L_3, as can be seen more clearly in Fig. 4.7, where the complete equipotential energy curves, acting as zero-velocity curves for a given energy, are represented schematically on the whole (x, y) plane. Note that at the three Lagrange points, the equipotential curves have the typical cross-shape of an unstable equilibrium position, just as in the problem of the inverted oscillator we studied in Chapter 1. If Fig. 4.7 represents, say, the Earth–Moon system, a rocket leaving the Earth must have sufficient energy to get at least to L_1 in order to reach the Moon. With more energy, it can escape the system through L_2 behind the Moon, or with even more energy from L_3 behind the Earth.

Besides these unstable equilibrium points, there are (not at all intuitively) two other Lagrange points, L_4 and L_5, where the

---

[4]We will meet Lagrange again in Chapter 6.

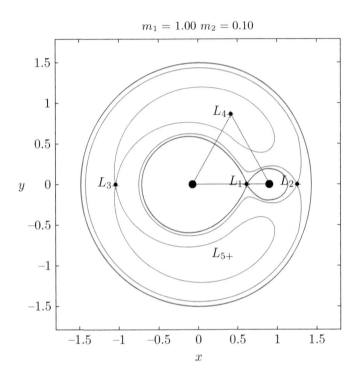

Fig. 4.7. Equipotential curves and Lagrange points ($m_1 = 1$ and $m_2 = 0.1$).

equilibrium is stable! Each of these points are at the vertices of an equilateral triangle with the particle at one of the vertices and the two massive bodies at the other two vertices. Let us prove this statement.

From Fig. 4.7, it can be seen that the third vertex of the said equilateral triangle is located at

$$x_4 = \mu - \frac{1}{2}, \quad y_4 = \pm\frac{\sqrt{3}}{2},$$

and it can be shown with some tedious but simple algebra that the first and second derivatives at these points are

$$\Omega_x = 0, \quad \Omega_y = 0,$$

$$\Omega_{xx} = \frac{3}{8}, \quad \Omega_{yy} = \frac{9}{8}, \quad \Omega_{xy} = \pm 3\frac{\sqrt{3}}{4}(\mu - 1/2) \tag{4.23}$$

(we use the shorthand notation $\Omega_x = \partial\Omega/\partial x(x_4, y_4)$, $\Omega_{xx} = \partial^2\Omega/\partial x^2(x_4, y_4)$, etc.).

Now, quite generally, any function $\Omega(x, y)$ with a maximum or minimum at (x_4, y_4) can be expanded in a Taylor series as

$$\Omega(x, y) = \Omega(x_4, y_4) + \frac{1}{2}\Omega_{xx}\Delta x^2 + \Omega_{xy}\Delta x\Delta y + \frac{1}{2}\Omega_{yy}\Delta y^2, \quad (4.24)$$

around the point (x_4, y_4), with $\Delta x = x - x_4$ and $\Delta y = y - y_4$. Thus the equations of motion (4.18) near this point reduce to

$$\begin{aligned}
\Delta\ddot{x} - \Delta\dot{y} &= \Omega_{xx}\Delta x + \Omega_{xy}\Delta y, \\
\Delta\ddot{y} + \Delta\dot{x} &= \Omega_{xy}\Delta x + \Omega_{yy}\Delta y,
\end{aligned} \quad (4.25)$$

which are the same as the equations for two coupled oscillators. Following the same method as in Section 1.5 of Chapter 1, we set

$$\Delta x = ae^{\lambda t}, \quad \Delta y = be^{\lambda t}$$

and rewrite (4.25) in matrix form:

$$\begin{pmatrix} \lambda^2 - \Omega_{xx} & -2\lambda - \Omega_{xy} \\ -2\lambda - \Omega_{xy} & \lambda^2 - \Omega_{yy} \end{pmatrix} \begin{pmatrix} a \\ b \end{pmatrix} = 0. \quad (4.26)$$

The determinant of the 2×2 matrix above is

$$\lambda^4 - (\Omega_{xx} + \Omega_{yy} + 4)\lambda^2 + \Omega_{xx}\Omega_{yy} - \Omega_{xy}^2,$$

and it must be equated to zero for the above equations to have non-trivial solutions. After substituting the values of Ω_{xx}, etc., given by (4.23), we find that

$$\lambda^4 + \frac{5}{2}\lambda^2 + \frac{27}{16}\,\mu(1 - \mu) = 0, \quad (4.27)$$

with solution

$$\lambda^2 = \frac{5}{4}\left(-1 \pm \sqrt{1 - 27\mu(1 - \mu)/25}\right).$$

Now, it is easy to check that the term under the square root, for $0 < \mu < 1$, is limited between $73/100$ and 1, and therefore, $\lambda^2 < 0$ and λ is *always* imaginary. Thus, any slight deviation from L_4 and L_5 oscillates as $\exp i|\lambda|t$ around these points, which thus correspond to stable positions. Obviously, the same procedure applies to the symmetrical L_5 point, with $x_5 = x_4$ and $y_5 = -y_4$.

The Sun–Jupiter system has precisely a set of asteroids, called the *trojans*, trapped in the corresponding stable L_4 and L_5 Lagrange points of the system. In the Earth–Moon system, the collinear Lagrange points are very convenient to position long distance satellites. These points are close enough to the Earth, and though their positions are unstable, satellites can be adjusted to stay there for a long time with minimal intervention. The famous James Webb Space Telescope, for instance, has been located at the point L_2 of the Sun-Earth system.

In some binary stellar systems, the stars may be so close together that the material of one of them is absorbed by the other. This is the case if one of the stars has so much expanded its atmosphere that it overfills its corresponding *Roche lobe*, which is just the equipotential surface with its apex at the intermediate Lagrange point L_1 (see Fig. 4.7). The material of the inflated star flows to its companion through the intermediate L_1 point.

The Laser Interferometer Space Antenna (LISA) is a very ambitious project for the detection of gravitational waves, waiting for its approval in some distant future. The original project was about placing two or three spacecrafts at the Lagrange points of the Sun–Earth systems to form a interferometer with a length of several million kilometers. Such an instrument would be able to detect low frequency gravitational waves of cosmic origin.

Chapter 5

Extended Rigid Bodies

Up to this point, we have considered the motion of bodies that can be approximated as point particles. That is the case, for instance, of a planet orbiting the Sun: its size is much smaller than the orbit and can therefore be approximated by a point. However, there are other problems in which it is necessary to take into account the finite size of the body under study. This chapter is devoted to the motion of solid bodies of finite size.

5.1. Tensor of inertia

First of all, let us see how to describe the orientation of a rigid body of arbitrary shape. The simplest way is to imagine a set of three orthogonal axes fixed inside the body, with the origin O in the center of mass (CM) or any other point in the body, as shown in Fig. 5.1. In order to characterize the orientation of the body, three parameters are needed, for instance, three rotations in a given order around each of the three axes of the body or the three Euler angles, as we will see in the following sections. To specify the position of the body in the three-dimensional space, we also need three coordinates to localize the point O. In total, any solid body is characterized precisely by six parameters: three for its orientation and three for its position in space.

Now, having chosen the origin O of the fixed coordinates system, the velocity of any point inside a rigid body can be decomposed into the sum of the velocity of O and its velocity of rotation, with angular

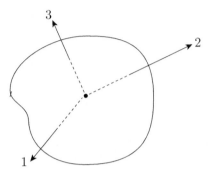

Fig. 5.1. Fixed axes.

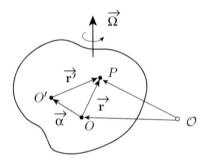

Fig. 5.2. Fixing a point in the body.

velocity Ω, around an axis $\boldsymbol{\Omega}$. Accordingly, as seen in Fig. 5.2, the total velocity $\mathbf{v}$ of any point P fixed inside the body is

$$\mathbf{v} = \mathbf{V} + \boldsymbol{\Omega} \times \mathbf{r}, \tag{5.1}$$

where $\mathbf{V}$ is the velocity of the origin O with respect to a fixed exterior origin $\mathcal{O}$ and $\mathbf{r}$ is the vector from O to the point P.

Before proceeding, let us see what happens if another origin of coordinates, say O', is chosen inside the body instead of O. Let $\mathbf{a}$ be the vector from O to O' as seen in Fig. 5.2; then $\mathbf{r} = \mathbf{r}' + \mathbf{a}$, where $\mathbf{r}'$ is the new position vector of P with respect to O'. Thus,

$$\mathbf{v} = \mathbf{V} + \boldsymbol{\Omega} \times \mathbf{r}' + \boldsymbol{\Omega} \times \mathbf{a}. \tag{5.2}$$

But $\mathbf{v} = \mathbf{V'} + \boldsymbol{\Omega'} \times \mathbf{r'}$ (all primed vectors are with respect to O'), and therefore,

$$\mathbf{V'} = \mathbf{V} + \boldsymbol{\Omega} \times \mathbf{a} + (\boldsymbol{\Omega} - \boldsymbol{\Omega'}) \times \mathbf{r'}.$$

However, the velocity of O' in the system of O is $\mathbf{V'} = \mathbf{V} + \boldsymbol{\Omega} \times \mathbf{a}$, from where it follows that

$$\boldsymbol{\Omega'} = \boldsymbol{\Omega}.$$

In other words, the angular velocity vector $\boldsymbol{\Omega}$ is a uniquely well-defined quantity for any solid rotating body, as it is independent of the origin from where it is measured. Of course, it is more natural, in most cases, to use the CM as origin, but this is not mandatory.

Let us now calculate the kinetic energy T of the solid body. First, imagine the body as a large set of N point particles, each with mass m_n located at a position $\mathbf{r_n}$ and with velocity $\mathbf{v_n}$ with respect to the CM. Thus,

$$T = \sum_{n}^{N} \frac{m_n}{2} v_n^2 = \sum_{n}^{N} \frac{m_n}{2} (\mathbf{V} + \boldsymbol{\Omega} \times \mathbf{r_n})^2, \tag{5.3}$$

from where it follows, explicitly, that

$$T = \sum_{n}^{N} \frac{m_n}{2} \left[V^2 + 2\mathbf{V} \cdot (\boldsymbol{\Omega} \times \mathbf{r_n}) + (\boldsymbol{\Omega} \times \mathbf{r_n}) \cdot (\boldsymbol{\Omega} \times \mathbf{r_n}) \right]. \tag{5.4}$$

Now, the total mass is $M = \sum_n m_n$ and the velocity term V^2, being common to all particles, can be factored out. As for the second term on the right-hand side of this last equation, it is a vectorial triple product and it vanishes because each term is equal to $\mathbf{r_n} \cdot (\mathbf{V} \times \boldsymbol{\Omega})$ and the term $(\mathbf{V} \times \boldsymbol{\Omega})$ is a constant that can be factored out of the summation, leaving $\sum_n m_n \mathbf{r_n} = 0$ by the very definition of the CM. Finally, the third term is $\Omega^2 r_n^2 - (\boldsymbol{\Omega} \cdot \mathbf{r_n})^2$.

Summing up, we have

$$T = \frac{M}{2} V^2 + \frac{1}{2} \sum_{n}^{N} m_n [\Omega^2 r_n^2 - (\boldsymbol{\Omega} \cdot \mathbf{r_n})^2], \tag{5.5}$$

or in the continuum limit,

$$T = \frac{M}{2}V^2 + \frac{1}{2}\int dV\rho(\mathbf{r})[\Omega^2 r^2 - (\mathbf{\Omega}\cdot\mathbf{r})^2], \tag{5.6}$$

where ρ is the mass density. It is understood that the summation or the integration are performed in the coordinate system fixed to the body.

From these last formulas, it follows that the total kinetic energy contains a term related to the motion of the CM and an additional kinetic term due to the rotation of the body. This second term can be rewritten as

$$T_{\text{rot}} \equiv \frac{1}{2}\sum_{i,j=1,2,3}\Omega_i\Omega_j I_{ij}, \tag{5.7}$$

where

$$I_{ij} \equiv \sum_n^N m_{(n)}[r_{(n)}^2\delta_{ij} - x_{(n)i}x_{(n)j}] \tag{5.8}$$

(label (n) refers to each of the N particles) or in the continuum limit

$$I_{ij} \equiv \int dV\rho(\mathbf{r})[r^2\delta_{ij} - x_ix_j]. \tag{5.9}$$

This is the *tensor of inertia*. As a tensor in three dimensions,[1] it can be expressed as a matrix:

$$\mathbb{I} = \int dV\rho(\mathbf{r}) \begin{pmatrix} y^2+z^2 & -xy & -xz \\ -xy & x^2+z^2 & -yz \\ -xz & -yz & x^2+y^2 \end{pmatrix} \tag{5.10}$$

(or an equivalent form for a discrete set of particles). Note that $\mathbb{I}$ is a symmetric matrix. As a matrix, it can be diagonalized by properly

---

[1] A tensor is a generalization of a vector. For our purposes in this text, it is enough to interpret the tensor of inertia as a 3×3 symmetric matrix M_{ij}, where indices i and j refer to row and column, respectively.

choosing the coordinate axes. Thus, quite generally, the tensor of inertia can always be brought to the form

$$\mathbb{I} = \text{diag}(I_1, I_2, I_3)$$

if the axes are chosen according to the symmetries of the body. The rotational kinetic energy thus reduces to

$$T_{\text{rot}} = \frac{1}{2}(I_1\Omega_1^2 + I_2\Omega_2^2 + I_3\Omega_3^2).$$

It is important to note that the tensor $\mathbb{I}$ must be evaluated with the origin of coordinates O at the CM, located at $\mathbf{r}_{\text{CM}}$, since this is the basic assumption in the derivation of (5.5). However, in practice, it may be easier to calculate a tensor $\mathbb{I}'$, exactly as defined in (5.8) or (5.9), but with the origin O' translated to an arbitrary point at $\mathbf{r}_{\text{CM}} + \mathbf{a}$ (see Fig. 5.2). Explicitly,

$$I'_{ij} \equiv \int dV \rho(\mathbf{r})[(r')^2 \delta_{ij} - x'_i x'_j], \tag{5.11}$$

and since $\mathbf{r}' = \mathbf{r} - \mathbf{a}$, we have

$$I'_{ij} = \int dV \rho(\mathbf{r})[(r^2 - 2\mathbf{a} \cdot \mathbf{r} + a^2)\delta_{ij} - x_i x_j + a_i x_j + a_j x_i - a_i a_j], \tag{5.12}$$

but there are three terms linear in x_i that vanish after integration since they are referred to the CM. It then follows finally that the correct tensor of inertia, defined with the origin at the CM, is

$$I_{ij} = I'_{ij} - M(a^2 \delta_{ij} - a_i a_j). \tag{5.13}$$

A similar procedure permits to calculate the tensor of inertia of a body composed of various pieces, such that the tensor of inertia of each piece is known separately. Consider then two or more bodies rigidly joined together. Let the CM of the complete system be at the point O, which will be taken as the origin of coordinates, and let each piece have its own CM at O_k, with the vectors $\mathbf{a}^{(k)}$ joining O

to O_k. The full tensor of inertia is

$$I_{ij} = \sum_{(k)} \int dV^{(k)} \rho(\mathbf{r}^{(k)})[(r^2 \delta_{ij} - x_i x_j],$$

where the integrals are over the whole system and the vector $\mathbf{r}$ is common to all the pieces. However, inside each body,

$$\mathbf{r} = \mathbf{r}^{(k)} + \mathbf{a}^{(k)},$$

where $\mathbf{r}^{(k)}$ is taken with respect to its individual CM O_k. Substituting this form of $\mathbf{r}$ in the previous formula for I_{ij}, and taking into account that

$$\int dV^{(k)} \rho(\mathbf{r}^{(k)}) \mathbf{r}^{(k)} = \mathbf{0}$$

by the definition of CM, we finally obtain the formula

$$I_{ij} = \sum_{(k)} I_{ij}^{(k)} + \sum_{(k)} M^{(k)} [(a^{(k)})^2 \delta_{ij} - a_i^{(k)} a_j^{(k)}], \qquad (5.14)$$

where $I_{ij}^{(k)}$ is the tensor of inertia of body k, if taken separately, and $M^{(k)}$ is its mass. Explicitly,

$$I_{ij}^{(k)} \equiv \int dV^{(k)} \rho(\mathbf{r}^{(k)})[(r^{(k)})^2 \delta_{ij} - x_i^{(k)} x_j^{(k)}].$$

An example will be worked out in this chapter.

5.2. The tensor of inertia for various shapes

Before considering some practical problems, let us work out the tensor of inertia for a few typical examples of solid bodies.

5.2.1. *A triangular configuration*

Three massive particles are located at the vertices of an isosceles triangle, as shown in Fig. 5.3. Two particles of equal mass m_1 are located at points $(-a/2, 0)$ and $(a/2, 0)$, and the third, of mass m_2,

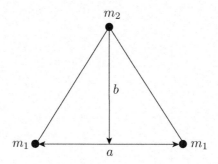

Fig. 5.3. Triangular configuration.

at $(0, b)$. Let us first calculate the position $(0, h)$ of the CM; it is

$$h = \frac{m_2 b}{2m_1 + m_2}.$$

Accordingly, the origin of coordinates must be shifted to that point and the particles have new coordinates $(-a/2, -h)$, $(a/2, -h)$ and $(0, b - h)$. It then follows, from the definition (5.8),

$$I_1 = 2m_1 h^2 + m_2 (b - h)^2,$$

$$I_2 = \frac{1}{2} m_1 a^2,$$

$$I_3 = \frac{1}{2} m_1 (a^2 + 4h^2) + m_2 (b - h)^2.$$

Note that the tensor of inertia is diagonal, since we have chosen the natural coordinate axis for this problem.

5.2.2. *Cylinder*

Consider a homogeneous cylinder of height h and radius R, as in Fig. 5.4, with the CM at the origin of coordinates. The density of matter ρ is homogeneous and limited by $|z| < h/2$ and $r < R$, where $r = \sqrt{x^2 + y^2}$. Using polar coordinates

$$x = r \cos \phi, \quad y = r \sin \phi,$$

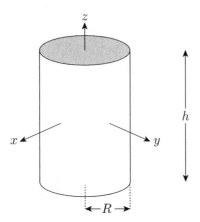

Fig. 5.4. Cylinder.

we find, according to (5.10),

$$\mathbb{I} = \rho \int_{-h/2}^{h/2} dz \int_0^{2\pi} d\phi \int_0^R dr\, r$$

$$\times \begin{pmatrix} r^2 \sin^2\phi + z^2 & -r^2 \sin\phi\cos\phi & -zr\cos\phi \\ -r^2 \sin\phi\cos\phi & r^2 \cos^2\phi + z^2 & -zr\sin\theta \\ -zr\cos\phi & -zr\sin\theta & r^2 \end{pmatrix}.$$

The integrals can be easily performed and the final result is

$$\mathbb{I} = \frac{1}{4}M \begin{pmatrix} R^2 + h^2/3 & 0 & 0 \\ 0 & R^2 + h^2/3 & 0 \\ 0 & 0 & 2R^2 \end{pmatrix}, \qquad (5.15)$$

where M is the mass of the cylinder ($M = \pi R^2 h\rho$).

Two limiting cases are as follows:

$h = 0$: a completely flat disk in the (x, y) plane.
$R = 0$: a rod of length h and negligible width oriented along the z axis.

5.2.3. *Tube*

For a straight homogeneous hollow tube of radius R, height h and negligible thickness, we can follow a similar calculation as for the cylinder. The tensor of inertia turns out to be, according to (5.10),

$$\mathbb{I} = \frac{1}{2}M \begin{pmatrix} R^2 + h^2/6 & 0 & 0 \\ 0 & R^2 + h^2/6 & 0 \\ 0 & 0 & 2R^2 \end{pmatrix}, \qquad (5.16)$$

where $M = 2\pi R h \sigma$ is the mass of the tube and σ its surface density. The limit $h = 0$ corresponds to a circular ring of negligible thickness.

5.2.4. *Homogeneous sphere*

For a homogeneous sphere of radius R, it is enough to note that the trace of $\mathbb{I}$ is

$$\text{Trace}(\mathbb{I}) = 8\pi\rho \int_0^R dr\, r^4 = \frac{6}{5}MR^2$$

(an integration over all angles yields the factor 4π); here, $M = (4\pi/3)R^3\rho$ is the mass of the sphere. Due to the symmetry of the problem,

$$I_1 = I_2 = I_3 = \frac{2}{5}MR^2 \qquad (5.17)$$

for the solid sphere.

If the sphere is hollow and consists only of a spherical shell, then with the same argument as above, the trace of $\mathbb{I}$ is

$$\text{Trace}(\mathbb{I}) = 8\pi\sigma R^4 = 2MR^2,$$

where σ is the surface mass density and $M = 4\pi R^2 \sigma$ is the mass of the shell. Thus

$$I_1 = I_2 = I_3 = \frac{2}{3}MR^2 \qquad (5.18)$$

for the hollow shell.

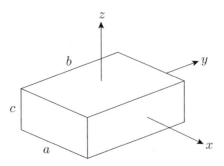

Fig. 5.5. Solid slab.

5.2.5. *Solid slab*

Consider now a homogeneous parallelepiped of sides a, b and c, as in Fig. 5.5. Then

$$I_1 = a\rho \int_{-b/2}^{b/2} dy \int_{-c/2}^{c/2} dz (y^2 + z^2) = \frac{M}{12}(b^2 + c^2),$$

$$I_2 = \frac{M}{12}(a^2 + c^2),$$

$$I_3 = \frac{M}{12}(a^2 + b^2),$$

where $M = abc\rho$ is the mass of the slab.

The limiting case of a thin sheet in the (x, y) is obtained, setting $c = 0$.

5.2.6. *Homogeneous cone*

Consider a homogeneous cone of radius R, height h and opening angle α $(R/h = \tan \alpha)$, as shown in Fig. 5.6. Let us first calculate the tensor I'_{ij} with respect to the vertex of the cone, as this is easier. Using cylindrical coordinates, we have

$$I'_1 = \rho \int dV (y^2 + z^2)$$

$$= \rho \int_0^h dz \int_0^{z \tan \alpha} dr\, r \int_0^{2\pi} d\phi (r^2 \sin^2 \phi + z^2). \qquad (5.19)$$

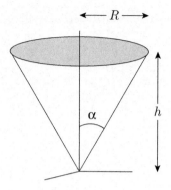

Fig. 5.6. Cone.

After some straightforward algebra,

$$I_1' = \frac{3}{5}M\left(\frac{R^2}{4} + h^2\right), \tag{5.20}$$

where

$$M = \frac{\pi}{3}hR^2\rho$$

is the mass of the homogeneous cone. A similar calculation yields

$$I_1' = I_2'$$

and

$$I_3' = \frac{3}{10}MR^2. \tag{5.21}$$

The above calculations have been performed with the vertex of the cone at the origin of coordinates. To calculate the tensor of inertia, we first note that the CM is located on the z axis and that according to (3.12), it must be at a distance a from the vertex given by

$$a = \frac{\int dV\, z\rho(\mathbf{r})}{M} = \frac{1}{(\pi/3)hR^2}(2\pi)\int_0^h dz \int_0^{zR/h} dr\, rz, \tag{5.22}$$

from where it follows that

$$a = \frac{3}{4}h.$$

Using (5.13) with $\mathbf{a} = (0, 0, a)$, the (diagonalized) components I_i turn out to be

$$I_1 = I_2 = \frac{3}{20} M \left(R^2 + \frac{h^2}{4} \right), \quad I_3 = \frac{3}{10} M R^2, \qquad (5.23)$$

calculated with respect to the CM, as it should be.

5.2.7. *Ellipsoid*

An ellipsoid is defined by the equation

$$\frac{x^2}{a^2} + \frac{y^2}{b^2} + \frac{z^2}{c^2} = 1,$$

where a, b and c are the semiaxes. The tensor of inertia can easily be calculated defining new coordinates $\bar{x} = x\, a/R$, $\bar{y} = y\, b/R$ and $\bar{z} = x\, c/R$, thus obtaining the same formulas as for a sphere of radius R. It then follows from the definition (5.10) that

$$I_1 = \frac{M}{5}(b^2 + c^2), \quad I_2 = \frac{M}{5}(a^2 + c^2), \quad I_3 = \frac{M}{5}(a^2 + b^2), \quad (5.24)$$

simply comparing with the corresponding formula for a sphere.

5.2.8. *Bicycle*

So far, we have considered only homogeneous configurations. As an example of a non-homogeneous configuration, consider the following problem. Two flat disks, each of mass M and radius R, are joined together at their axes by a bar of length L and negligible mass. Taking the CM of the system at the origin, and setting the coordinates system as shown in Fig. 5.7, we have

$$\mathbf{a}^{(1)} = (-L/2, 0, 0), \quad \mathbf{a}^{(2)} = (L/2, 0, 0)$$

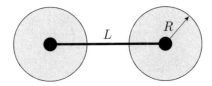

Fig. 5.7. Bicycle.

in the notation used for (5.14). Thus, using this same formula (5.14) together with (5.15) (with $h = 0$), we easily find

$$\mathbb{I} = \frac{M}{2}\text{diagonal}[R^2, R^2 + L^2, 2R^2 + L^2]. \qquad (5.25)$$

5.3. Rolling and rotating bodies

We now illustrate the use of the above formalism solving some problems that involve solid bodies subject to some particular force, such as gravity. Before proceeding, it must be clear that the total force acting on a body is the sum of all the forces acting on each of its parts, and if (and only if) the force is uniform, it acts as if the total mass were concentrated in the CM. This would be the case of the gravitational force if taken as approximately constant on the surface of the Earth, and this is the situation we will consider in the following. Otherwise, over large distances, tidal effects are important if the force is not uniform (as seen in Section 2.4 of Chapter 2).

5.3.1. *Down an inclined plane*

Consider the problem of a sphere (or a cylinder) of radius R rolling down a plane with an inclination angle α, as in Fig. 5.8. The total energy is

$$E = \frac{1}{2}MV^2 + \frac{1}{2}I_3\Omega^2 + Mg'x, \qquad (5.26)$$

where x is the distance over the plane, as shown in Fig. 5.8. The acceleration is $g' = g\sin\alpha$, and the velocity of the sphere is $V = \Omega R$ if it rolls down without sliding. Since $I_3 = (2/5)MR^2$ for a solid sphere, we have

$$E = M\left(\frac{1}{2}V^2 + \frac{1}{5}V^2 + g'x\right) = \frac{7}{5}M\left(\frac{1}{2}V^2 + \frac{5}{7}gx\right), \qquad (5.27)$$

implying that the sphere rolls down with an acceleration $(5/7)g\sin\alpha$ instead of g' (the common factor $7M/5$ is irrelevant since it does not affect the equation of motion). If it is a cylinder instead of a sphere, the acceleration would be $(2/3)g\sin\alpha$ with the same argument.

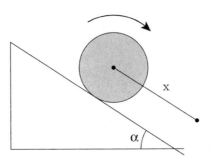

Fig. 5.8. Rolling body.

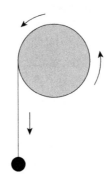

Fig. 5.9. Rotating pulley.

5.3.2. *Rotating pulley*

A mass m is hanging from a rope winded around a freely rotating pulley, as in Fig. 5.9. The pulley is a homogeneous cylinder of mass M and radius R. What is the acceleration of the mass as it unravels down? The component I_{zz} of the tensor of inertia, in Eq. (5.15), is the one that corresponds to the rotation of the pulley. Thus, the total energy of the system is

$$E = \frac{1}{2}\left(m\dot{y}^2 + \frac{M}{2}R^2\Omega^2 \right) + mgy,$$

where y is the height of the mass m. Clearly, $\dot{y} = -\Omega R$, and thus,

$$E = \frac{1}{2}\left(m + \frac{M}{2} \right)\dot{y}^2 + mgy,$$

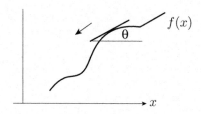

Fig. 5.10. Sliding ski.

implying that the acceleration of the unraveling mass is

$$g' = \frac{g}{1 + M/2m}.$$

5.3.3. *Sliding ski*

Consider a ski sliding down along a given path defined as the curve $y = f(x)$ in the vertical (x, y) plane. The ski always remains tangent to this curve, which means that if θ is its angle with respect to the x axis, as shown in Fig. 5.10, then

$$\tan \theta = f'(x),$$

where $f'(x) = df(x)/dx$ is the tangent angle to the curve.

The energy (per unit mass m) of the ski is

$$E = \frac{1}{2}(\dot{x}^2 + \dot{y}^2) + \frac{I}{2m}\dot{\theta}^2 + gy, \qquad (5.28)$$

where I is the component of the tensor of inertia with respect to its rotation axis (perpendicular to the (x, y) plane).

Deriving the conditions $y = f(x)$ and $\tan \theta = f'(x)$, we have

$$f'(x)\dot{x} = \dot{y}, \quad f'(x)\dot{x} = \sec^2 \theta \, \dot{\theta}, \qquad (5.29)$$

and after substitution in the energy equation, we arrive at

$$\frac{1}{2}\left[1 + (f')^2 + \frac{I}{m}\left(\frac{f''}{1 - (f')^2}\right)^2\right]\dot{x}^2 + gf = E, \qquad (5.30)$$

an equation involving only the x coordinate which can be solved by quadratures once the form of the curve $y = f(x)$ is given, together with the energy given by the initial conditions (for instance, $E = gy_0$ if the ski starts to slide down from rest at a height y_0).

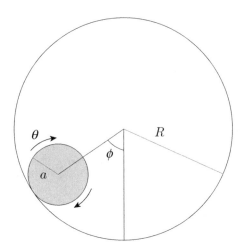

Fig. 5.11. Cylinder inside cylinder.

5.3.4. *Rolling cylinder*

A homogeneous cylinder of radius a and mass m rolls without sliding inside a cylindrical cavity of radius R. Let ϕ be the angle subtended between the vertical and the CM of the cylinder, as in Fig. 5.11. If the cavity is fixed, the velocity of the CM is

$$V = (R - a)\dot{\phi}.$$

Note that if the cylinder rotates at an angle θ, it will roll along an arc of circle $a\theta$ inside the cavity. The angle subtended by this arc with respect to the axis of the cavity is $a\theta/R$. Therefore, $a\theta = R\phi$.

Now, the cylinder has two rotational motions: one around its own axis and another around the axis of the cavity. The angular velocity of the former is $\dot{\theta} = (R/a)\dot{\phi}$ and that of the latter is $\dot{\phi}$. Accordingly, the total angular velocity of the cylinder is

$$\Omega = \left(\frac{R}{a} - 1\right)\dot{\phi},$$

with both terms being of opposite signs, since a clockwise rotation of the cylinder rolls it counterclockwise inside the cavity (and *vice versa*).

Summing up, the kinetic energy of the cylinder is

$$T = \frac{1}{2}mV^2 + \frac{1}{2}I_3\frac{(R-a)^2}{a^2}\dot{\phi}^2$$

$$= \frac{1}{2}\left[m + \frac{I_3}{a^2}\right](R-a)^2\dot{\phi}^2. \tag{5.31}$$

Using the value of I_3 from (5.15) and including the gravitational potential, the total energy turns out to be

$$E = \frac{3}{4}m(R-a)^2\dot{\phi}^2 + mg(R-a)(1-\cos\phi).$$

Compare this with the energy of a simple pendulum (1.11): the cylinder oscillates inside the cavity just as a pendulum. For small oscillations around the equilibrium position $\phi = 0$, the frequency of oscillations is $\omega = \sqrt{2g/3(R-a)}$.

5.3.5. *Rolling cone*

A homogeneous cone (height h, basis radius R, opening angle 2α, $\tan\alpha = h/R$) is rolling without sliding over a plane horizontal surface, as shown in Fig. 5.12. To calculate its kinetic energy, note that the cone has two rotational motions: one around its symmetry axis and another around its vertex, the cone always resting on the plane. Let θ be the angle between a given axis on the plane and the contact of the cone with that plane, and ϕ the rotation angle of the cone, as seen in Fig. 5.12. The rotational velocity of the cone

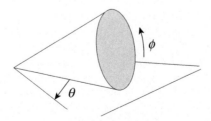

Fig. 5.12. Rolling cone.

at its basis is

$$V = \frac{h}{\cos \alpha} \dot{\theta} = R\dot{\phi} = h \tan \alpha \, \dot{\phi},$$

from where we deduce the relation $\sin \alpha \, \dot{\phi} = \dot{\theta}$ between the two angular velocities. It then follows that the components of the total angular momentum, with respect to the principal axis of the cone, as shown in Fig. 5.12, are

$$\Omega_1 = -\cos \alpha \, \dot{\theta}, \quad \Omega_2 = 0, \quad \Omega_3 = -\sin \alpha \, \dot{\theta} + \frac{\dot{\theta}}{\sin \alpha} = -\frac{\cos \alpha^2}{\sin \alpha} \dot{\theta}.$$

As in the previous case of the cylinder, the two terms in Ω_3 are of opposite signs because a counterclockwise rotation of the cone around its axis moves it clockwise on the plane (and *vice versa*).

The total kinetic energy of the cone is accordingly

$$T = \frac{1}{2} M a^2 \cos \alpha^2 + \frac{1}{2} I_1 \cos^2 \alpha \, \dot{\theta}^2 + \frac{1}{2} I_3 \frac{\cos^4 \alpha}{\sin^2 \alpha} \dot{\theta}^2,$$

where the first term corresponds to the kinetic energy due to the motion of the CM, located a distance a from the vertex of the cone. Using the parameters of the cone given in Section 5.2.6, we find with some simple algebra

$$T = \frac{3}{40} M h^2 (1 + 5 \cos^2 \alpha) \dot{\theta}^2.$$

5.3.6. *Solid pendulum*

Consider a solid pendulum, such as a sphere of mass M and radius R hanging from a rod of length l with negligible mass, as shown in Fig. 5.13. Since the CM is at a distance $l + R$, the total energy of the system is

$$E = \frac{1}{2} M (l + R)^2 \dot{\phi}^2 + \frac{1}{2} I \dot{\phi}^2 - M g (l + R) \cos \phi \qquad (5.32)$$

if the oscillations are in a plane. For a solid sphere, $I = \frac{2}{5} M R^2$. Then comparing with the energy of a simple pendulum, it follows that the

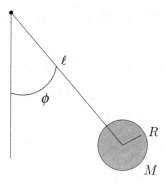

Fig. 5.13. Solid pendulum.

frequency is

$$\omega^2 = \frac{g(l + R)}{(l + R)^2 + \frac{2}{5}R^2}$$

for small oscillations.

5.4. Angular velocity and torque

From the previous study, the angular momentum of a solid body is

$$\mathbf{L} = \int dV \rho(\mathbf{r}) \mathbf{r} \times (\mathbf{\Omega} \times \mathbf{r})$$

$$= \int dV \rho(\mathbf{r})[\mathbf{\Omega} r^2 - (\mathbf{\Omega} \cdot \mathbf{r})\mathbf{r}].$$

Comparing with (5.10), it can also be written as

$$L_i = \sum_j I_{ij}\Omega_j. \tag{5.33}$$

Thus, an alternative notation is

$$\mathbf{L} = \mathbb{I}\mathbf{\Omega}, \tag{5.34}$$

where $\mathbb{I}$ is the tensor of inertia we discussed at the beginning of this chapter (a 3×3 matrix with components I_{ij}).

Accordingly, we have the following suggestive equivalence between linear and circular motion:

$$\mathbf{p} = m\mathbf{v} \rightarrow \mathbf{L} = \mathbb{I}\boldsymbol{\Omega}, \tag{5.35}$$

$$\mathbf{F} = \frac{d}{dt}\mathbf{p} \rightarrow \mathbf{K} = \frac{d}{dt}\mathbf{L}, \tag{5.36}$$

$$T = \frac{1}{2}\sum mv_i^2 \rightarrow T_{\text{rot}} = \frac{1}{2}\sum I_{ij}\Omega_i\Omega_j, \tag{5.37}$$

where $\mathbf{K}$ is the torque.

5.4.1. *Hitting a billiard ball*

What is the optimum height to hit (horizontally) a billiard ball if we want it to roll without sliding. Suppose that we hit a ball of radius R and mass M at a height h (as in Fig. 5.14) with a force $F = MdV/dt$, where V is the linear velocity acquired by the ball. The applied torque is then $(h - R)F$.

If we want the ball to roll without sliding, then $V = \Omega R$, and therefore,

$$F = MR\frac{d\Omega}{dt}.$$

But according to Eqs. (5.35) and (5.36), the change in angular momentum is the torque:

$$\frac{d}{dt}L = I\frac{d}{dt}\Omega = (h - R)F,$$

and comparing the last two equations, it follows that

$$MR(h - R) = I. \tag{5.38}$$

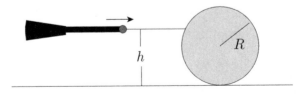

Fig. 5.14. Billiard ball.

Since $I = (2/5)MR^2$ for a solid sphere, it follows that $h = (7/5)R$ is the optimum height to hit the ball.

5.4.2. *Angular velocity and momentum*

It is important to note that according to formulas (5.34), the angular velocity $\boldsymbol{\Omega}$ and the angular momentum $\mathbf{L}$ *are not parallel*, except in the very special case of a spherically symmetric body with all its diagonal components I_i being equal, namely a sphere. Otherwise, even for an *axially symmetric* body, $I_1 = I_2 \neq I_3$, these two vectors are not parallel, nor are they parallel to the symmetry axis of the body. The implications can be noted from the analysis in the following section.

5.4.3. *Axisymmetric bodies*

As we have seen, the angular momentum vector $\mathbf{L}$ is constant if there are no external torques acting on the body. If this is the case, we can choose the coordinate system as in Fig. 5.15: the axis x_3 in the direction of the symmetry axis, and the vector $\mathbf{L}$ in the $(1,3)$ plane, that is, $\mathbf{L} = (L_1, 0, L_3)$, and therefore, $\boldsymbol{\Omega} = (L_1/I_1, 0, L_3/I_3)$, implying that $\mathbf{L}$, $\boldsymbol{\Omega}$ and the symmetry axis x_3 are all in the same $(1,3)$ plane.

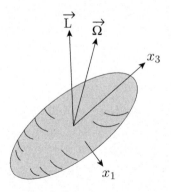

Fig. 5.15. Rotating axisymmetric top.

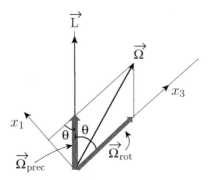

Fig. 5.16. Angular momentum and angular velocity.

Now, as shown in Fig. 5.16, let θ be the angle between $\mathbf{L}$ and x_3; then $L_3 = L\cos\theta$, and thus, $\Omega_3 = (L/I_3)\cos\theta$.

Accordingly, we can decompose the vector $\mathbf{\Omega}$ into two components: one component $\mathbf{\Omega}_{\rm rot}$ along the x_3 symmetry axis and the other component $\mathbf{\Omega}_{\rm prec}$ along the angular momentum vector $\mathbf{L}$; the magnitude of the latter is $\Omega_{\rm prec} = \Omega_1/\sin\theta$ as is evident form Fig. 5.16. However, $\Omega_1 = L_1/I_1 = (L\sin\theta)/I_1$ and thus,

$$\Omega_{\rm prec} = \frac{L}{I_1}. \tag{5.39}$$

The physical interpretation of this result is as follows. The body rotates with angular velocity $\Omega_{\rm rot}$ around its own symmetry axis, but it also undergoes a motion of *precession* around the vector $\mathbf{L}$ with an angular velocity $\Omega_{\rm prec}$. This is the typical motion of a spinning top. A more detailed analysis will be presented in the following sections.

5.4.4. *Asymmetric bodies*

The problem of a rotating body which is fully asymmetric, even without torques, is quite complicated, but a qualitative analysis can be performed with relative ease.[2] For this purpose, it must be noted that there are two constants of motion, the total energy E and the

---

[2]For a complete analysis, see, e.g., Landau and Lifshitz, *Mechanics*.

total angular momentum L, both given by

$$2E = \frac{L_1^2}{I_1} + \frac{L_2^2}{I_2} + \frac{L_3^2}{I_3}, \tag{5.40}$$

$$L^2 = L_1^2 + L_2^2 + L_3^2. \tag{5.41}$$

Suppose for definitiveness that $I_1 < I_2 < I_3$. Then, in the space of $\mathbf{L}$, the first equation (5.40) describes an ellipsoid with semiaxis major $\sqrt{2EI_1}$ and semiaxis minor $\sqrt{2EI_3}$, while the second equation (5.41) describes a sphere with radius L. It also follows from these two equations above that the condition

$$2EI_1 < L^2 < 2EI_3$$

is always satisfied, implying that the ellipsoid and the sphere always intersect on a curve, as shown in Fig. 5.17. This curve is called *polhode*.[3] As the solid body rotates, the vector $\mathbf{L}$, in its own space, moves with its tip on the polhode. However, the angular momentum is actually constant in the physical space and, therefore, one must visualize the ellipsoid, with its polhode, moving while keeping $\mathbf{L}$ constant.

The important point is that the polhode reduces to a small closed circuit around the L_1 and L_3 axes, which is typical of stable motions, and has an X-form around the L_2 axis, which is typical of unstable motions, as we have already seen. The implication is that the rotation

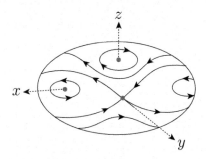

Fig. 5.17. Polhode.

---

[3]From Greek, *hode*: way, path.

of a solid body around a principal axis $L_i \propto x_i$ is stable if it is the axis with the larger or the smaller value of I_i, but is unstable in the intermediate case.

5.5. Euler angles

As mentioned before, three parameters are necessary to fully specify the orientation of a solid body. These three parameters can be the successive rotations around each of the three axes in a fixed reference frame. Another possibility, which turns out to be more convenient for many calculations, is in terms of the *Euler angles*.[4] These angles permit one to relate the coordinate axes of a fixed system, say, X, Y, Z, to the coordinates as measured in a system moving with the solid body, say, x_1, x_2, x_3, as shown in Fig. 5.18.

Let us start with the X axis: rotate it at an angle ϕ around the Z axis, and call the new X axis the *nodal* axis.

Next, rotate the Z axis at an angle θ around the nodal axis. The new Z axis is the x_3 axis.

Then rotate the nodal axis at an angle ψ around the x_3 axis. The nodal axis becomes now the x_1 axis.

Finally, rotate the x_1 axis at an angle $\pi/2$ around the x_3 axis, and thus, define the x_2 axis.

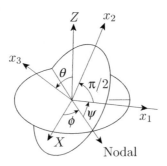

Fig. 5.18. Euler angles.

---

[4]Leonhard Euler (1707–1783), most distinguished Swiss mathematician and physicist.

Quite generally, a rotation can be described as a superposition of three rotations: a rotation ϕ around the Z axis, followed by a rotation θ around the nodal axis, and then a rotation ψ around the x_3 axis. Thus, the angular velocity vectors $\boldsymbol{\Omega}$ is the sum of these three rotations that are explicitly

$$\dot{\phi}\hat{\mathbf{Z}}, \quad \dot{\theta}\hat{\mathbf{n}}, \quad \dot{\psi}\hat{\mathbf{x}}_3,$$

where $\hat{\mathbf{Z}}$, $\hat{\mathbf{n}}$ and $\hat{\mathbf{x}}_3$ are the unit vectors in the directions of the Z axis, the nodal axis and the x_3 axis, respectively. These three unit vectors can be referred to the comoving axes x_1, x_2, x_3; as seen in Fig. 5.18,

$$\hat{\mathbf{Z}} = (\sin\theta\sin\psi, \sin\theta\cos\psi, \cos\theta),$$

$$\hat{\mathbf{n}} = (\cos\psi, -\sin\psi, 0),$$

$$\hat{\mathbf{x}}_3 = (0, 0, 1).$$

Accordingly, the components of an angular velocity vector $\boldsymbol{\Omega}$ are, in the x_i basis,

$$\Omega_1 = \dot{\theta}\cos\psi + \dot{\phi}\sin\theta\sin\psi,$$

$$\Omega_2 = -\dot{\theta}\sin\psi + \dot{\phi}\sin\theta\cos\psi, \qquad (5.42)$$

$$\Omega_3 = \dot{\phi}\cos\theta + \dot{\psi}.$$

If the x_i axes are chosen as the principal axes of the rotating body, then the rotational kinetic energy is

$$T_{\text{rot}} = \frac{1}{2}(I_1\Omega_1^2 + I_2\Omega_2^2 + I_3\Omega_3^2). \qquad (5.43)$$

In the particular case of an symmetric top such that $I_1 = I_2$, the above formula somewhat simplifies to

$$T_{\text{rot}} = \frac{1}{2}I_1(\dot{\theta}^2 + \sin^2\theta\,\dot{\phi}^2) + \frac{1}{2}I_3(\dot{\phi}\cos\theta + \dot{\psi})^2. \qquad (5.44)$$

Note that, due to the symmetry of the body, ψ does not appear in the formula for the energy since it is the angle around the symmetry axis.

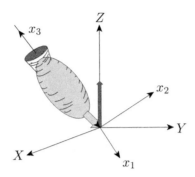

Fig. 5.19. Rotating top.

Moreover, in this case, the angular momentum, which is $L_i = I_i \Omega_i$, is given by

$$L_1 = I_1 \dot{\theta}, \quad L_2 = I_1 \sin\theta\,\dot{\phi}, \quad L_3 = I_3(\cos\theta\,\dot{\phi} + \dot{\psi}).$$

For a freely rotating body, without torques acting on it, the angular momentum vector is constant. We can choose it along the fixed Z axis, in which case, according to Fig. 5.19,

$$L_1 = 0, \quad L_2 = L\sin\theta, \quad L_3 = L\cos\theta,$$

implying that $\dot{\theta} = 0$, $L = I_1\dot{\phi}$ and $L\cos\theta = I_3(\cos\theta\,\dot{\phi} + \dot{\psi})$. We recognize $\dot{\phi}$ as the angular velocity of precession, $\dot{\psi}$ as the angular velocity of rotation, and θ as the inclination angle, everything in accordance with (5.39) above and the related discussion.

5.5.1. *Euler equations*

We have seen at the beginning of this chapter that the time derivative of the velocity, or any vector A, measured in a fixed system is related to the time derivative of the same vector in the rotating system according to

$$\left(\frac{d\mathbf{A}}{dt}\right)_{\text{fixed}} = \left(\frac{d\mathbf{A}}{dt}\right)_{\text{rotating}} + \mathbf{\Omega} \times \mathbf{A}.$$

The components of the time derivatives in the rotating system are simply the time derivatives of the components in this system, as projected on the x_i axis fixed in the body. Applying this argument to the linear momentum $\mathbf{P}$ and the angular momentum $\mathbf{L}$, we have according to (5.35) and (5.36),

$$\frac{d\mathbf{P}}{dt} + \mathbf{\Omega} \times \mathbf{P} = \mathbf{F},$$

$$\frac{d\mathbf{L}}{dt} + \mathbf{\Omega} \times \mathbf{L} = \mathbf{K}.$$

Explicitly,

$$\frac{dP_1}{dt} + \Omega_2 P_3 - \Omega_3 P_2 = F_1, \tag{5.45}$$

$$\frac{dP_2}{dt} + \Omega_3 P_1 - \Omega_1 P_3 = F_2, \tag{5.46}$$

$$\frac{dP_3}{dt} + \Omega_1 P_2 - \Omega_2 P_1 = F_3, \tag{5.47}$$

and

$$I_1 \frac{d\Omega_1}{dt} + \Omega_2 I_3 \Omega_3 - \Omega_3 I_2 \Omega_2 = K_1, \tag{5.48}$$

$$I_2 \frac{d\Omega_2}{dt} + \Omega_3 I_1 \Omega_1 - \Omega_1 I_3 \Omega_3 = K_2, \tag{5.49}$$

$$I_3 \frac{d\Omega_3}{dt} + \Omega_1 I_2 \Omega_2 - \Omega_2 I_1 \Omega_1 = K_3, \tag{5.50}$$

where $\mathbf{F}$ and $\mathbf{K}$ are the applied force and torque, respectively.

5.5.2. *Axisymmetric bodies*

The above equations somewhat simplify in the case of rotating symmetric bodies ($I_1 = I_2$), since

$$I_3 \frac{d\Omega_3}{dt} = K_3.$$

In particular, if the body rotates freely without a torque acting on it, then Ω_3 is constant. The other equations, in this case, are

$$I_1 \frac{d\Omega_1}{dt} + (I_3 - I_1)\Omega_3\, \Omega_2 = 0,$$
$$I_1 \frac{d\Omega_2}{dt} - (I_3 - I_1)\Omega_3\, \Omega_1 = 0, \tag{5.51}$$

with solution

$$\Omega_1 + i\Omega_2 \propto e^{i\omega t},$$

where $\omega = (I_3/I_1 - 1)\Omega_3$; this is the frequency of precession. As for the angular velocity of rotation around the symmetry axis, it is

$$\Omega_3 = \frac{L}{I_3} \cos\theta,$$

in accordance with the previous analysis on axisymmetric bodies.

5.5.3. *Asymmetric bodies*

Let us consider now the rotation of an asymmetric body, such that all I_i's are different. Suppose for simplicity that there is no external torque and that the body is rotating around one of its principal axis, say, x_3. Then, in a zeroth-order approximation, $\mathbf{\Omega} = (0, 0, \Omega)$, Euler's equation (5.48) imply that Ω is constant. In a first-order approximation, keeping only terms linear in Ω_1 and Ω_2, these equations take the form

$$I_1\dot{\Omega}_1 + (I_3 - I_2)\Omega\Omega_3 = 0, \tag{5.52}$$
$$I_2\dot{\Omega}_2 + (I_1 - I_3)\Omega\Omega_1 = 0, \tag{5.53}$$
$$I_3\dot{\Omega}_3 + (I_2 - I_1)\Omega\Omega_2 = 0, \tag{5.54}$$

and thus,

$$\ddot{\Omega}_1 + \frac{(I_3 - I_2)(I_3 - I_1)}{I_1 I_2}\Omega^2\Omega_1 = 0. \tag{5.55}$$

This is the equation of a harmonic oscillator; we know that its condition for stability is

$$(I_3 - I_2)(I_3 - I_1) > 0, \tag{5.56}$$

otherwise the rotational motion is unstable. For a stable rotation, we need either $I_3 > I_2$ and $I_3 > I_1$ or $I_3 < I_2$ and $I_3 < I_1$.

Let us apply this result to an ellipsoid having three different semiaxes a, b, c, with $x_3 \sim c$. The three components I_i are given by (5.24) and, according to our result, the rotation is stable if $(b^2 - c^2)(a^2 - c^2)$ is positive. This is the case if the rotation is around the smallest axis $(c < a, \ c < b)$ or around the largest axis $(c > a, \ c > b)$, but a rotation around the intermediate axis $(c > a, \ b > c \ \text{or} \ c < a, \ b < c)$ is unstable.[5] A similar analysis applies to a homogeneous slab. All this is consistent with our previously obtained result on asymmetric bodies.

In the following chapter, we study the motion of rotating bodies in more detail using the formulas obtained in this chapter.

---

[5]There is a complete theory of rotating ellipsoidal bodies, with applications to astrophysics. Chandrasekhar (1987).

Chapter 6

Lagrangian Formulation

This chapter is devoted to the formalism of Lagrange,[1] which, together with the Hamiltonian formalism (see Chapter 7), is the core of analytical mechanics. The basic idea of the Lagrangian formalism is the following. Until now, we have used mainly Cartesian or, occasionally, spherical coordinates, adapted to the geometry of each particular problem. However, a mechanical system may be constrained to move with some restrictions, and a particular coordinate system may be the most appropriate to deal with the problem. For instance, a spherical pendulum moves in a three-dimensional space, but its motion is restricted to a sphere that can be described by two coordinates, and the force acting along the string is compensated by its tension (Newton's third law!). Another simple example is a particle moving on a fixed surface (Fig. 6.1); the force of gravity acting on the particle has two components, one parallel to the surface and another perpendicular to it: it is only the first force that produces motion, while the latter is compensated by the reaction of the surface and does not contribute to the motion.

6.1. Constraints and generalized coordinates

In the terminology used in the eighteenth century, any force applied on a particle was said to be decomposed into a "living force", which produces motion, and a "dead force", which does not as it

---

[1] Joseph Louis Lagrange (1736–1813), Italian born French mathematician and astronomer.

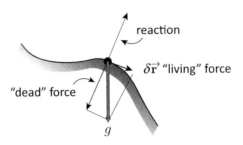

Fig. 6.1. "Dead" force and virtual displacement.

is due to constraints only. Let us call them $\mathbf{F}_{(\text{motion})}$ and $\mathbf{F}_{(\text{constraint})}$, respectively.

Quite generally, if a mechanical system can be described by N parameters, but is subject to C constraints, it has actually only $N - C$ *degrees of freedom*. For instance, $N = 3$ and $C = 1$ for the spherical pendulum, or $N = 6$ and $C = 1$ for two point particles in a three-dimensional space tied together with a rigid rod. Accordingly, to each degree of freedom, we can associate a *virtual displacement*, $\delta\mathbf{r_i}$, which is a displacement that the system is free to perform, at least in principle.

Now, as noted by D'Alembert,[2] the constraining forces must always be perpendicular to the virtual displacement (as seen, for instance, in Fig. 6.1):

$$\mathbf{F}_{\mathbf{i}(\text{constraint})} \cdot \delta\mathbf{r_i} = 0. \tag{6.1}$$

Accordingly, since the total force is the sum $\mathbf{F}_{\mathbf{i}(\text{constraint})} + \mathbf{F}_{\mathbf{i}(\text{motion})}$, Newton's second law can be rewritten in a form known as *D'Alembert's principle*:

$$\sum_i \mathbf{F}_{\mathbf{i}(\text{constraint})} \cdot \delta\mathbf{r_i} = \sum_i (m_i \ddot{\mathbf{r}}_\mathbf{i} - \mathbf{F}_{\mathbf{i}(\text{motion})}) \cdot \delta\mathbf{r_i} = 0. \tag{6.2}$$

The following simple example illustrates the meaning and utility of the D'Alembert principle. Consider two masses m_1 and m_2 hanging

---

[2] Jean le Rond d'Alembert (1717–1783), French mathematician, physicist and philosopher.

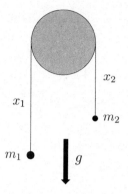

Fig. 6.2. Pulley and virtual displacements.

on each side of a freely rotating pulley of negligible mass, as in Fig. 6.2. The equations of motion of this system are

$$m_1 \ddot{x}_1 - m_1 g = -\tau_1,$$
$$m_2 \ddot{x}_2 - m_2 g = -\tau_2, \tag{6.3}$$

where τ_1 and τ_2 are the tension forces in the string uniting the two masses. Clearly, if the length of the string is fixed, the constraint is that $x_1 + x_2$ must be constant.

Now, the virtual displacements of the two masses are δx_1 and δx_2 and the constraint forces are τ_1 and τ_2. According to D'Alembert's principle (6.1), the last pair of equations imply that

$$\tau_1 \, \delta x_1 + \tau_2 \, \delta x_2 = 0,$$

together with the constraint

$$\delta x_1 + \delta x_2 = 0,$$

and these two conditions imply that the tensions on each end of the string must be equal: $\tau_1 = \tau_2 \equiv \tau$. Then equations in (6.3) imply with some simple algebra

$$\ddot{x}_1 = -\ddot{x}_2 = g \frac{m_1 - m_2}{m_1 + m_2}$$

and

$$\tau = 2g\mu,$$

where $\mu = m_1 m_2/(m_1 + m_2)$ is the reduced mass. We have thus obtained the acceleration of the system and the magnitude of the tensions.

After this simple example, let us return to the most general case and apply the above discussion to the case of n particles in a three-dimensional space, subject to C constraints. In principle, the system of particles should be described by $N = 3n$ coordinates, but there are actually $F = 3n - C$ degrees of freedom. Accordingly, we only need F *generalized coordinates*, $(q_1, q_2, \ldots, q_F)$, to characterize the whole system.

Now, if $\mathbf{r_i}$ is the position of particle number i, then

$$\mathbf{r_i} = \mathbf{r_i}(q_1, q_2, \ldots, q_F, t) \tag{6.4}$$

in terms of the F generalized coordinates (the only ones we need). Therefore,

$$\delta \mathbf{r}_i = \sum_{k=1}^{F} \frac{\partial \mathbf{r}_i}{\partial q_k} \delta q_k,$$

and thus, for any set of applied forces $\mathbf{F}_i$,

$$\sum_{i=1}^{N} \mathbf{F}_i \cdot \delta \mathbf{r_i} = \sum_{i=1}^{N} \mathbf{F}_i \cdot \sum_{k=1}^{F} \frac{\partial \mathbf{r}_i}{\partial q_k} \delta q_k = \sum_{k=1}^{F} \left(\sum_{i=1}^{N} \mathbf{F}_i \cdot \frac{\partial \mathbf{r}_i}{\partial q_k} \right) \delta q_k. \tag{6.5}$$

It must be noted that, due to the D'Alembert principle (6.1), the constraint forces make no contribution to this last relation, and therefore, $\mathbf{F}_i$ contribute as "living" forces only.

Accordingly, this last formula suggests defining the F *generalized forces* as

$$Q_k \equiv \sum_{i=1}^{N} \mathbf{F}_i \cdot \frac{\partial \mathbf{r}_i}{\partial q_k} \tag{6.6}$$

(recalling that $k = 1, 2, \ldots, F$) such that

$$\sum_{i=1}^{N} \mathbf{F}_i \cdot \delta \mathbf{r}_i = \sum_{i=1}^{N} m_i \ddot{\mathbf{r}}_i \cdot \delta \mathbf{r}_i = \sum_{k=1}^{F} Q_k \, \delta q_k \tag{6.7}$$

in accordance with the D'Alembert principle.

The important point evidenced by this last equation is that there are only F components of the generalized forces on the right-hand side instead of the N components of the whole system on the left-hand side. The F components are the ones that really matter.

As for the kinetic energy, it is given by

$$T = \sum_{i=1}^{N} \frac{1}{2} m_i \dot{\mathbf{r}}_i \cdot \dot{\mathbf{r}}_i$$

in terms of the coordinates $\mathbf{r}_i$, but it can be rewritten in terms of the generalized coordinates q_i and $\dot{q}_i$. This can be achieved with some tedious but straightforward algebra, which we leave to Appendix A. The following important equation is obtained from formula (A.6):

$$\frac{d}{dt}\left(\frac{\partial T}{\partial \dot{q}_i}\right) - \frac{\partial T}{\partial q_i} = Q_i. \tag{6.8}$$

This is called the Lagrange equation of second kind. It is Newton's second law in terms of the generalized forces Q_i.

In the important case of a generalized force that depends on a potential $V(q_i)$, we can set

$$Q_i = -\frac{\partial V}{\partial q_i},$$

and therefore, defining the Lagrangian function $\boxed{L = T - V}$, we obtain the fundamental Lagrange equations:

$$\boxed{\frac{d}{dt}\left(\frac{\partial L}{\partial \dot{q}_i}\right) - \frac{\partial L}{\partial q_i} = 0.} \tag{6.9}$$

There are as many coordinates q_i as degrees of freedom and, in practice, one must choose the appropriate coordinates compatible with the constrictions of a system under study.

Actually, the Lagrangian L that appears in the Lagrange equations is a fundamental function that does not necessarily have the form $T - V$. It appears quite naturally in the principle of minimal action, as we will see in the following section.

6.2. Variational problems

Before proceeding to work out some applications of the Lagrange equations, let us give a general interpretation in terms of the *principle of minimal action*, also known as the *Hamilton principle*.

The variational calculus is an important branch of mathematics since it is related to the problem of *minimal action*, which is related in turn to the Lagrangian formulation of mechanics. The basic idea is the following. Suppose we choose a totally arbitrarily curve in q space defined by the function $q_i(t)$, and we define the *action* as the *functional* (i.e., a function of function)

$$A \equiv \int_{t_1}^{t_2} dt \, L(q_i(t), \dot{q}_i(t), t), \qquad (6.10)$$

where L is a certain function of $q_i(t)$, its first derivative $\dot{q}_i(t)$ with respect to t, and possibly t itself. The limits of integration are fixed at t_1 and t_2. The function L can be any function of its arguments, though we will identify it later with the Lagrangian, and t can be any parameter (to be identified later as time) describing the curve $q_i(t)$ $(i = 1, \ldots, N)$ in the $(N + 1)$-dimensional space $(q_i(t), t)$, as seen in Fig. 6.3.

Now, the problem is to determine the form of $q_i(t)$ such that, for a given function L, the functional A has an extremal value (minimum or maximum). In order to illustrate the procedure, let us consider a

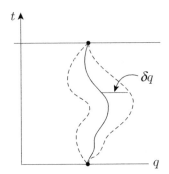

Fig. 6.3. Physically possible and not possible trajectories.

one-dimensional problem, since a generalization to more dimensions is obvious enough.

Consider the functional given by (6.10) for a certain trajectory $q(t)$ and suppose that we also calculate $A + \delta A$ for another somewhat closer trajectory $q(t) + \delta q(t)$, with the same initial and final positions as the former one, as seen in Fig. 6.2. Thus,

$$A + \delta A = \int_{t_1}^{t_2} dt\, L(q(t) + \delta q(t), \dot{q}_i(t) + \delta \dot{q}(t), t), \qquad (6.11)$$

from where it follows that in a first approximation,

$$\delta A = \int_{t_1}^{t_2} dt \left(\frac{\partial L}{\partial q} \delta q + \frac{\partial L}{\partial \dot{q}} \delta \dot{q} \right) \qquad (6.12)$$

plus terms of order δq^2 that can be neglected for our present purpose. This last equation can be rewritten as

$$\delta A = \int_{t_1}^{t_2} dt \left[\frac{\partial L}{\partial q} \delta q + \frac{d}{dt} \left(\frac{\partial L}{\partial \dot{q}} \delta q \right) - \frac{d}{dt} \left(\frac{\partial L}{\partial \dot{q}} \right) \delta q \right], \qquad (6.13)$$

and the second term in the square brackets, being an exact derivative, can be integrated immediately and does not contribute to the integral since $\delta q(t_1) = \delta q(t_2) = 0$, as it was assumed from the beginning. Thus,

$$\delta A = \int_{t_1}^{t_2} dt \left[\frac{\partial L}{\partial q} - \frac{d}{dt} \left(\frac{\partial L}{\partial \dot{q}} \right) \right] \delta q, \qquad (6.14)$$

and the term in square brackets must be identically zero since the integral must vanish for any δq.

Clearly, in more than one dimension, $L(q_i, \dot{q}_i, t)$, and we have

$$\delta A = \int_{t_1}^{t_2} dt \sum_i \left[\frac{\partial L}{\partial q_i} - \frac{d}{dt} \left(\frac{\partial L}{\partial \dot{q}_i} \right) \right] \delta q_i = 0, \qquad (6.15)$$

and since all δq_i are independent among them, we deduce that

$$\frac{\partial L}{\partial q_i} - \frac{d}{dt} \left(\frac{\partial L}{\partial \dot{q}_i} \right) = 0, \qquad (6.16)$$

which are called, quite generally, the *Euler–Lagrange equations*. It is the Lagrange equation of mechanics (6.9) we have just derived.

Thus, the Lagrangian can also be defined as the function that makes the action (6.10) an extremal when the physically possible trajectory is chosen among the others. This is the Hamilton principle. Further applications of the variational principles will be given in Chapter 8.

6.3. Illustrative problems

At this point, it is worth noting that the Lagrange equations directly provide a constant of motion if the Lagrangian does not depend on a certain variable, say, X, but only on its time derivative. Then, according to the Euler–Lagrange equations, $\partial L / \partial \dot{X}$ is a constant of motion.[3] In this case, X is called a *cyclic coordinate*.

6.3.1. *Central force*

Let us return to the problem studied in Chapter 2 of a planet subject to a central force. The Lagrangian (per unit mass) is

$$L = \frac{1}{2}(\dot{r}^2 + r^2\dot{\phi}^2) + \frac{GM}{r}$$

(compare with (2.15)), assuming for simplicity that the motion is in a plane (as already proved). Since

$$\frac{\partial L}{\partial \dot{\phi}} = r^2\dot{\phi},$$

it immediately follows that

$$l \equiv r^2\dot{\phi}$$

is a constant of motion: it is the angular momentum per unit mass. Thus, the Euler–Lagrange equation for the coordinate r reduces to

$$\ddot{r} = -\frac{GM}{r^2} + \frac{l^2}{r^3}, \tag{6.17}$$

---

[3]This is the simplest version of the more general Noether theorem due to Emmy Noether (1882–1935): the invariance of a Lagrangian under a given transformation implies the conservation of a certain quantity.

as already known. Note that the conservation of angular momentum follows directly from the fact that the Lagrangian depends on $\dot\phi$ but not on ϕ, which is a cyclic coordinate in the sense explained above.

6.3.2. *Kepler problem with dipole correction*

It is known that the Sun or the Earth are slightly bulged at the equator due to their rotation. How does this affect their satellites? We can reproduce this bulging as an additional dipole term, as seen in Chapter 2. Accordingly, the Lagrangian of the problem in spherical coordinates is

$$L = \frac{1}{2}(\dot r^2 + r^2\dot\theta^2 + r^2\,\sin^2\theta\,\dot\phi^2) + \frac{GM}{r} - p\frac{\cos\theta}{r^2}, \qquad (6.18)$$

where p is the dipole. Since ϕ is a cyclic coordinate, the angular momentum (per unit mass) is conserved as usual:

$$l = r^2\sin^2\theta\,\dot\phi.$$

The Lagrange equations are now

$$\ddot r = r\dot\theta^2 + \frac{l^2}{r^3\sin\theta} - \frac{GM}{r^2} + 2p\frac{\cos\theta}{r^3}, \qquad (6.19)$$

$$\frac{d}{dt}(r^2\dot\theta) = \frac{l^2\cos\theta}{r^2\sin^3\theta} + p\frac{\sin\theta}{r^2}. \qquad (6.20)$$

These are two coupled equations that can be solved numerically. However, it is more instructive to note that planets move in almost circular orbits and the dipole does not make a notable contribution. Accordingly, we look for solutions of the form

$$r = R + \delta r, \quad \theta = \pi/2 + \delta\theta,$$

with constant R as the orbital radius. Neglecting terms of order δ^2 and higher (and thus $\sin\theta \approx 1$ and $\cos\theta \approx -\delta\theta$), the above Lagrange equations reduce, with some simple algebra, to the compact forms

$$\frac{d^2}{dt^2}(\delta r \pm R\,\delta\theta) = -\frac{1}{R^4}(GMR \pm 2p)(\delta r \pm R\,\delta\theta) \pm \frac{p}{R^3}. \qquad (6.21)$$

As can be checked by direct substitution, the solutions of this pair of equations are

$$\delta r \pm R\, \delta\theta = \frac{pR}{GMR \pm 2p} + K\cos(\omega_\pm t),\qquad(6.22)$$

where

$$\omega_\pm^2 = \frac{1}{R^4}(GMR \pm 2p)\qquad(6.23)$$

and K is an arbitrary constant to be determined by initial conditions. We see that a small equatorial bulge of the Sun produces a very slight oscillation around the circular orbit of a planet moving in the same plane as the bulge. Instability will occur only in the extreme (and unlikely) case, $GMR < 2p$.

6.3.3. *Spherical pendulum*

Let us return to the spherical pendulum studied in Chapter 1. The Lagrangian (per unit mass) is

$$L = \frac{1}{2}R^2(\dot\theta^2 + \sin\theta^2\,\dot\phi^2) + gR\cos\theta.$$

Since L does not depend on ϕ, we immediately deduce that

$$l \equiv \frac{\partial L}{\partial\dot\phi} = R^2\sin^2\theta\,\dot\phi$$

is a constant of motion: it is the angular momentum per unit mass. The other Euler–Lagrange equation is

$$\frac{d}{dt}(R^2\dot\theta) + R^2\sin\theta\cos\theta\,\dot\phi^2 + gR\sin\theta = 0.\qquad(6.24)$$

Of course, this last equation can be obtained directly as the derivative of the total energy, which is just the Lagrangian with the sign of the potential energy changed[4]:

$$E = \frac{1}{2}R^2(\dot\theta^2 + \sin\theta^2\,\dot\phi^2) - gR\cos\theta.$$

---

[4]A rigorous definition of energy, valid in full generality, as it follows from a Lagrangian, will be given in the following chapter within the Hamiltonian formalism.

Fig. 6.4. Vibrating pendulum.

Deriving this last equation with respect to time, one obtains Eq. (6.24) multiplied by $\dot\theta$. We thus recover the results obtained in Chapter 1.

6.3.4. *Vibrating pendulum*

A rigid pendulum, restricted to move in a vertical plane, is fixed to a vertically vibrating pivot point, as in Fig. 6.4. If Ω is the frequency of vibration of the pivot, the position of the pendulum bob is

$$\mathbf{r} = (l \sin\theta, \quad -l\cos\theta + R_0 \sin\Omega t), \tag{6.25}$$

and its velocity is

$$\dot{\mathbf{r}} = (l\cos\theta\,\dot\theta, \quad l\sin\theta\,\dot\theta + \Omega R_0 \cos\Omega t). \tag{6.26}$$

Accordingly, the exact Lagrangian (per unit mass) of the system is

$$L = \frac{1}{2}(l^2\dot\theta^2 + \Omega^2 R_0^2 \cos^2\Omega t) + l\Omega R_0 \sin\theta \cos\Omega t\,\dot\theta$$
$$+ g(l\cos\theta - R_0 \sin\Omega t). \tag{6.27}$$

There is only one degree of freedom corresponding to the coordinate θ. The Euler–Lagrange equation reduces, after some straightforward algebra, to

$$\ddot{\theta} + \left(\frac{g}{l} - \frac{\Omega^2 R_0}{l} \sin \Omega t\right) \sin \theta = 0. \tag{6.28}$$

Obviously for $\Omega = 0$, we recover the usual pendulum equation. For small oscillation ($\theta \ll 1$ and $\sin \theta \approx \theta$), the above equation reduces to a Mathieu equation (1.32) after redefining $\Omega t = 2\tau - \pi/2$. The interesting point is that for the pendulum standing vertically upright, we have $\theta = \pi + \delta$, and if $\delta \ll 1$ Eq. (6.28) takes the form

$$\frac{d^2 \delta}{dt^2} - \left(\frac{g}{l} - \frac{\Omega^2 R_0}{l} \sin \Omega t\right) \delta = 0, \tag{6.29}$$

which is also a Mathieu equation. As such, it admits stable motions for certain values of the dimensionless parameters $g/l\Omega^2$ and R_0/l. For these values, the oscillations of the vertically inverted pendulum are stable.[5]

6.3.5. *Damped oscillator (2)*

A simple example of a time-dependent Lagrangian is the damped oscillator. Defining a Lagrangian

$$L = \frac{m}{2}(\dot{x}^2 - \omega^2 x^2)e^{2\gamma t}, \tag{6.30}$$

it is easy to see that the equation of motion is just Eq. (1.24) in Chapter 1.

6.3.6. *The rolling coin*

A vertical coin is rolling on a horizontal plane. The coin has, in principle, four degrees of freedom: the two coordinates (x, y) giving its position on the plane, the angle ϕ giving its orientation with, say the x axis and its angle of rotation θ, as shown in Fig. 6.5. If the coin rolls without sliding, and ds is the differential element of length along

---

[5]It is sometimes called a *Kapitza oscillator* after Pyotr Kapitza (1894–1984) who studied it.

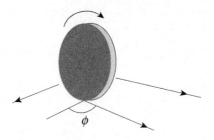

Fig. 6.5. Rolling coin.

its trajectory, then $ds = R\,d\theta$, where R as its radius. Accordingly,

$$dx = \cos\phi\,ds, \quad dy = \sin\phi\,ds,$$

giving two conditions to be taken into account:

$$\dot{x} = R\cos\phi\,\dot{\theta}, \qquad \dot{y} = R\sin\phi\,\dot{\theta}. \tag{6.31}$$

The Lagrangian of the system is

$$L = \frac{M}{2}(\dot{x}^2 + \dot{y}^2) + \frac{1}{2}I_3\dot{\theta}^2 + \frac{1}{2}I_1\dot{\phi}^2, \tag{6.32}$$

where M is the mass of the coin, I_3 and I_1 are the coefficients of inertia around the axis of the coin and around its diameter, respectively. Using the conditions (6.31), the Lagrangian simplifies to

$$L = \frac{1}{2}(MR^2 + I_3)\dot{\theta}^2 + \frac{1}{2}I_1\dot{\phi}^2,$$

from where the equations of motion follow simply as $\ddot{\theta} = 0$ and $\ddot{\phi} = 0$, with solutions

$$\theta = \theta_0 + at, \quad \phi = \phi_0 + bt,$$

where θ_0, ϕ_0, a, b are constants of motion. Returning to (6.31), the coordinates (x, y) can easily be integrated:

$$x = x_0 + \frac{aR}{b}\sin(\phi_0 + bt), \quad y = y_0 - \frac{aR}{b}\cos(\phi_0 + bt). \tag{6.33}$$

The coin rolls at constant velocity in a circle with a radius depending on the initial conditions. We can always choose the initial angle as

$\theta_0 = 0$ and the orientation of the coordinate axes such that $\phi_0 = 0$, with a and b being the initial rotational velocity and twist given to the coin.

6.3.7. *The symmetric top*

With the Lagrangian formalism, we are finally ready to analyze in detail the motion of a symmetric spinning top subject to gravity. Suppose the tip of the top is fixed at the origin of coordinates. From the previous chapter, we have the expression for the kinetic energy (5.44), and thus, together with the potential energy, the Lagrangian turns out to be

$$L = \frac{1}{2}(Ml^2 + I_1)(\dot{\theta}^2 + \sin^2\theta\,\dot{\phi}^2) + \frac{1}{2}I_3(\dot{\phi}\cos\theta + \dot{\psi})^2 - Mgl\cos\theta,$$

$$(6.34)$$

where M is the mass of the top and l is the distance from its tip to its center of mass. As usual, we are using spherical coordinates, as shown in Fig. 6.6: θ is the angle between the fixed Z coordinate and the axis of rotation x_3. Recall that the angle ψ describes the rotation of the top around its axis of symmetry and the angle ϕ its precession. The angle θ is a measure of the inclination of the top with respect to the vertical; this motion is called *nutation*.

First of all, note that the Lagrangian does not depend on the coordinates ϕ and ψ, which are cyclic coordinates, and thus, we

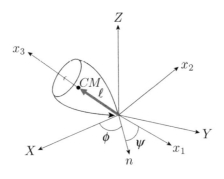

Fig. 6.6. Spinning top.

immediately find two constants of motion:

$$\frac{\partial L}{\partial \dot{\psi}} = I_3(\dot{\phi} \cos \theta + \dot{\psi}) \equiv L_3,$$

$$\frac{\partial L}{\partial \dot{\phi}} = ((Ml^2 + I_1) \sin^2 \theta + I_3 \cos^2 \theta) \dot{\phi} + I_3 \dot{\psi} \cos \theta \equiv L_Z,$$

and therefore,

$$\dot{\phi} = \frac{L_Z - L_3 \cos \theta}{(Ml^2 + I_1) \sin^2 \theta}, \tag{6.35}$$

$$\dot{\psi} = \frac{L_3}{I_3} - \frac{L_Z - L_3 \cos \theta}{(Ml^2 + I_1) \sin^2 \theta} \cos \theta. \tag{6.36}$$

There remains an equation for the coordinate θ, which is not cyclic. However, in this and similar cases (such as the spherical pendulum), the constant energy is actually the first integral of this equation. Accordingly, one can use directly the formula for the energy. In this case, it turns out to be, after substitutions of the above constants of motion,

$$E' = \frac{1}{2} I' \dot{\theta}^2 + U_{\text{eff}}(\theta), \tag{6.37}$$

where $U_{\text{eff}}(\theta)$ is an effective potential:

$$U_{\text{eff}}(\theta) = \frac{(L_Z - L_3 \cos \theta)^2}{2I' \sin^2 \theta} + Mgl \cos \theta, \tag{6.38}$$

and we have redefined

$$E' = E - \frac{L_3^2}{2I_3} + Mgl, \quad I' = Ml^2 + I_1.$$

Before proceeding with a detailed analysis, we can deduce from this last equation the condition for a spinning top to remain in a fully vertical position. The question is whether the position $\theta = 0$, implying $L_3 = L_Z(=I_3\Omega_3)$, is a stable solution. To see this, it is enough to notice that, for $L_Z = L_3$ and $\theta \ll 1$, Eq. (6.38) reduces to

$$U_{\text{eff}} \approx \left(\frac{L_Z^2}{8I'} - \frac{1}{2} Mgl \right) \theta^2,$$

from where we recover the equation of a harmonic oscillator, the condition for stability being

$$\omega^2 \equiv L_Z^2 - 4Mgl(Ml^2 + I_1) > 0,$$

where ω is the frequency of oscillation around the vertical.

Returning now to the general equation (6.37), we obtain

$$t = \int \frac{d\theta}{\sqrt{2(E' - U_{\text{eff}}(\theta))/I'}}. \tag{6.39}$$

Thus, we have reduced the problem to a quadrature relating time to the nutation angle θ. The remaining variables ψ and ϕ as functions of t can be obtained from (6.35) and (6.36).

The problem can be solved numerically, but it is more instructive to perform a qualitative analysis based on Eq. (6.35) and the total energy (6.37). First of all, note that there must be certain values θ_n of the nutation angle for which $\dot{\theta} = 0$. Indeed, Eq. (6.37) can be written explicitly as

$$E' \sin^2 \theta = \frac{1}{2} I' \sin^2 \theta \, \dot{\theta}^2 + \frac{1}{2I'} (L_Z - L_3 \cos \theta)^2 + Mgl \sin \theta^2 \cos \theta, \tag{6.40}$$

and the condition $\dot{\theta} = 0$ reduces this equation to a third-degree algebraic equation $f(\cos \theta) = 0$. A semi-qualitative graph is shown in Fig. 6.7. An inspection shows that the equation has two real physical roots such that $-1 \leq \cos \theta \leq 1$, which correspond to the angles θ_1 and θ_2 (a third solution, $\cos \theta > 1$, is not real). Thus, according to (6.40), the angle of nutation θ must be limited between these two values (which are also the limits of integration of (6.39)).

From our qualitative analysis, we deduce that there are three kinds of motion. According to (6.35), the precession $\dot{\phi}$ must be in the positive (counterclockwise) direction if $(L_Z - L_3 \cos \theta) > 0$ for all values of θ bounded by θ_1 and θ_2 (L_Z and L_3 are of the same sign, which we have taken as positive). If, on the other hand, there

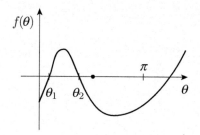

Fig. 6.7. Nutation angles at which $\dot{\theta} = 0$.

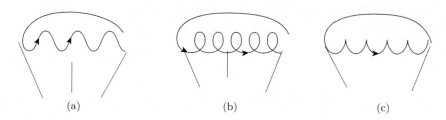

Fig. 6.8. Three possible nutational motions.

are certain values of θ such that $(L_Z - L_3 \cos \theta) < 0$, then for these values the precession changes its direction. These two typical motions of the top are shown in Figs. 6.8(a) and 6.8(b).

A third, intermediate, possibility corresponds to the limiting case $L_Z - L_3 \cos \theta_1 = 0$. In this particular case, it follows that both $\dot{\theta}$ and $\dot{\phi}$ vanish at θ_1 (but not at θ_2), and the trajectory turns out to be as shown in Fig. 6.8(c). This third possibility corresponds to the case when the top is kept spinning at a certain inclination angle θ_1 and suddenly released: the top falls at a certain angle and then rises again.

6.4. Constrained systems

The Lagrangian formulation is very useful if the degrees of freedom of a given system are explicitly known. In certain problems, however, it is not easy to deduce the degrees of freedom directly from the constraints imposed on the system. In such cases, it is convenient to use the method of *Lagrange multipliers*. The idea is to write the

Lagrangian with additional terms in the form

$$L(x_i, \dot{x}_i, t) + \sum_{\mu} \lambda_\mu F_\mu(x_i),$$

where

$$F_\mu(x_i) = 0,$$

($\mu = 1, \ldots, C$) are the C constraints on the system. The Lagrange multipliers λ_μ included in the modified Lagrangian are to be interpreted as variables. Then, since there are no $\dot{\lambda}_\mu$ terms in the Lagrangian, the Euler–Lagrange equations yield directly the constraints

$$\frac{\partial L}{\partial \lambda_\mu} = F_\mu(x_i) = 0.$$

Let us illustrate this method with an example in the following section.

6.4.1. *Falling dumbbell*

Two masses, m_1 and m_2, are falling freely, held together by a rigid rod of length l and negligible weight. The position of the two masses are $\mathbf{r}_1$ and $\mathbf{r}_2$, and therefore, the Lagrangian of the problem is

$$L = \frac{m_1}{2}\dot{\mathbf{r}}_1^2 + \frac{m_2}{2}\dot{\mathbf{r}}_2^2 - g(m_1 z_1 + m_2 z_2) + \frac{1}{2}\lambda[(\mathbf{r}_2 - \mathbf{r}_1)^2 - l^2], \quad (6.41)$$

where λ is the Lagrange multiplier and the last term in square brackets is the (single) constraint. The corresponding equations of motion, according to (6.9) and interpreting λ as another generalized coordinate, reduce to

$$m_1\ddot{\mathbf{r}}_1 = -\lambda(\mathbf{r}_2 - \mathbf{r}_1) - gm_1\hat{\mathbf{e}}_{\mathbf{z}},$$
$$m_2\ddot{\mathbf{r}}_1 = \lambda(\mathbf{r}_2 - \mathbf{r}_1) - gm_2\hat{\mathbf{e}}_{\mathbf{z}}, \quad (6.42)$$

and

$$2\frac{\partial L}{\partial \lambda} = (\mathbf{r}_2 - \mathbf{r}_1)^2 - l^2 = 0, \quad (6.43)$$

which is simply the constraint.

If we now define the center of mass

$$\mathbf{R}_{\mathrm{CM}} = \frac{m_1\mathbf{r}_1 + m_2\mathbf{r}_2}{m_1 + m_2}$$

and the relative position

$$\mathbf{r} = \mathbf{r}_2 - \mathbf{r}_1,$$

the above equations take the form

$$\ddot{\mathbf{R}} = -g\hat{\mathbf{e}}_{\mathbf{z}},$$

$$\ddot{\mathbf{r}} = \frac{\lambda}{\mu}\mathbf{r}, \tag{6.44}$$

where $\mu = m_1 m_2/(m_1 + m_2)$ is the reduced mass. From the second equation, we see that the Lagrange multiplier λ is the (constant) *tension* in the rod, and also that

$$\mathbf{r} \times \ddot{\mathbf{r}} = \frac{d}{dt}(\mathbf{r} \times \dot{\mathbf{r}}) = 0,$$

which is simply the conservation of the angular momentum.

Summing up, the dumbbell falls down with acceleration g, while rotating with constant angular velocity. As expected, the rotation does not affect the free fall: all bodies, independent of their proper motions, fall with the same acceleration in vacuum.

6.4.2. *Inside a figure of revolution*

Another illustrative problem is that of a particle sliding without friction inside a vertical figure of revolution defined, in cylindrical coordinates, as $z = f(r)$. The Lagrangian (per unit mass) is

$$L = \frac{1}{2}(\dot{r}^2 + r^2\dot{\phi}^2 + \dot{z}^2) - gz + \lambda(z - f(r)). \tag{6.45}$$

To begin with, since the Lagrangian does not depend explicitly on ϕ, we deduce that

$$\frac{\partial L}{\partial \dot{\phi}} = r^2\dot{\phi} \equiv l$$

is a constant of motion (it is the angular momentum of the particle). The other equations of motion are

$$\ddot{r} - \frac{l^2}{r^3} = -\lambda f'(r),$$
(6.46)

$$\ddot{z} + g = \lambda,$$
(6.47)

together with the constraint $z - f(r) = 0$; thus, λ can be identified with the change of the vertical acceleration due to the constraining surface. Eliminating λ,

$$\ddot{r} - \frac{l^2}{r^3} + f'(r)(\ddot{z} + g) = 0.$$
(6.48)

Multiplying this last equation by $\dot{r}$ and using $\dot{z} = f'(r)\dot{r}$, we can integrate once:

$$\frac{1}{2}[1 + (f'(r))^2]\dot{r}^2 + gf(r) + \frac{l^2}{2r^2} = E,$$
(6.49)

where E is the (constant) energy. This last equation can be solved by quadratures just as in (1.4), once the form of $f(r)$ has been given. (Of course, the same equation could have been deduced directly from the definition of energy.)

6.5. Holonomic and non-holonomic constraints

In the previous problems, the constraints were particular cases of a general kind of constraints having the form $F_\mu(q_i, t) = 0$ ($\mu = 1$ to C, the number of constraints), which simply implies that there are algebraic relations between all the coordinates (and possibly time). Such constraints are called *holonomic*.[6] Of course, a differentiation of the constraint equations yields the C conditions

$$\frac{\partial F_\mu}{\partial q_1}\dot{q}_1 + \frac{\partial F_\mu}{\partial q_2}\dot{q}_2 + \cdots + \frac{\partial F_\mu}{\partial t} = 0.$$

On the other hand, there are constraints that also involve first derivatives of the coordinates in the totally general forms $F_\mu(q_i, \dot{q}_i, t)$;

---

[6]In Greek, *holos*: whole, entire, *nomos*: law.

such constraints are called *non-holonomic*. A particular case (semi-holonomic) is that of C constraints of the form

$$\sum_{k=1}^{N} a_{\mu k}(q_k, t)\dot{q}_k + a_{\mu 0}(q_k, t)dt = 0, \quad \mu = 1, 2, \ldots, C \qquad (6.50)$$

on a system described by N coordinates q_k, where the terms $a_{\mu k}(q_k, t)$ are functions of the coordinates and possibly of time; therefore, there are only $N - C$ independent coordinates. In this case, however, there is no guarantee that the functions $a_{\mu k}(q_k, t)$ could be derived as the q_i derivatives of single functions $F_\mu(q_k, t)$.

Unfortunately, there is no known general method for dealing with non-holonomic constraints. One cannot use directly the method of Lagrange multipliers due to many subtleties, as is evident from the large number of articles written on the subject in the specialized literature.[7] The problem is that it is not clear how to deal with the constraint equations when varying the paths in the Lagrangian in the usual way, as we have seen in the beginning of this chapter. In any case, it can be seen that the Lagrange multipliers method is valid in general for quasi-holonomic constraints, such as (6.50). Let us see an illustrative problem.

6.5.1. *Sliding ski (2)*

Let us consider the problem of a ski sliding without friction on a plane surface inclined at an angle α. The constraint is that its major axis must remain tangent to its trajectory. If ϕ is the angle of its axis with respect to the x axis, as shown in Fig. 6.9, then the constraint is $\dot{y}/\dot{x} = \tan\phi$ or

$$\dot{x}\sin\phi - \dot{y}\cos\phi = 0. \qquad (6.51)$$

Accordingly, the Lagrangian is

$$L = \frac{M}{2}(\dot{x}^2 + \dot{y}^2) + \frac{I}{2}\dot{\phi}^2 + Mg'y + \lambda(\dot{x}\sin\phi - \dot{y}\cos\phi), \qquad (6.52)$$

---

[7]See, e.g., Flannery (2005), and references therein.

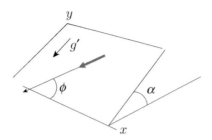

Fig. 6.9. Sliding ski.

where $g' = g \sin \alpha$, M is the mass and I the coefficient of inertia of the ski around its center of mass. The last term with the Lagrange multiplier λ takes the constraint into account.

The equations of motion turn out to be

$$M\ddot{x} + \frac{d}{dt}(\lambda \sin \phi) = 0, \tag{6.53}$$

$$M\ddot{y} - \frac{d}{dt}(\lambda \cos \phi) = Mg', \tag{6.54}$$

$$I\ddot{\phi} - \lambda(\dot{x}\cos\phi + \dot{y}\sin\phi) = 0, \tag{6.55}$$

together with the constraint (6.51). The first two equations can be directly integrated:

$$M\dot{x} + \lambda \sin \phi = c_1,$$

$$M\dot{y} - \lambda \cos \phi = c_2 + Mg't, \tag{6.56}$$

where c_1 and c_2 are integration constants. It follows from this last pair of equations and the constraint (6.51) that

$$\lambda = c_1 \sin \phi - (c_2 + Mg't)\cos\phi, \tag{6.57}$$

and also,

$$M^2 v^2 = c_1^2 + c_2^2 - \lambda^2 \tag{6.58}$$

for the velocity $v = \sqrt{\dot{x}^2 + \dot{y}^2}$.

It also follows from equations in (6.5.1) that

$$M(\dot{x}\cos\phi + \dot{y}\sin\phi) = c_1\cos\phi + (c_2 + Mg't)\sin\phi$$

$$= \left[\dot{\lambda} + Mg'\frac{d}{dt}(t\cos\phi)\right] \Big/ \dot{\phi}. \qquad (6.59)$$

Using Eqs. (6.55) and (6.58), we can show with some simple algebra that the time derivative of the kinetic energy is

$$\frac{d}{dt}\left(\frac{1}{2}I\dot{\phi}^2 + \frac{1}{2}Mv^2\right) = g'\lambda\frac{d}{dt}(t\cos\phi). \qquad (6.60)$$

As expected, the kinetic energy is conserved only if the motion takes place on a horizontal plane ($g' = 0$).

For numerical calculations, the basic equation (6.55) can also be written as

$$I\ddot{\phi} + (c_2 + Mg't)\dot{x} - c_1\dot{y} = 0. \qquad (6.61)$$

Summing up, we have identified the Lagrange multiplier and obtained a complete set of equations for the functions x, y and ϕ. Choosing the initial conditions, the rest is an exercise in numerical integration, but that issue is outside the scope of this book.

Chapter 7

Hamiltonian Formulation

Given a mechanical system with F degrees of freedom, the Lagrangian formalism permits one to deduce F equations of motion for the F generalized coordinates, which are *second*-order differential equations. An alternative approach is to redefine the first temporal derivatives of each generalized coordinate and thus obtain $2F$ differential equations of *first*-order. This is the approach taken by Hamilton[1] in his formulation of mechanics.

7.1. Generalized momenta

In the Hamiltonian formulation, one defines the *generalized momenta* as

$$p_i = \frac{\partial L}{\partial \dot{q}_i}, \tag{7.1}$$

starting with the most general Lagrangian $L(q_i, \dot{q}_1, t)$, and thus, the Euler–Lagrange equation (6.9) imply

$$\dot{p}_i = \frac{\partial L}{\partial q_i}. \tag{7.2}$$

The next step is to define the Hamiltonian function as

$$H(q_i, p_i, t) = \sum_i p_i \dot{q}_i - L(q_i, \dot{q}_i, t), \tag{7.3}$$

noting that it is a function of the generalized coordinates q_i and the generalized momenta p_i (and possibly of time t), while the

---

[1]William Rowan Hamilton (1805–1865), Irish physicist, mathematician and astronomer.

Lagrangian $L(q_i, \dot{q}_i, t)$ is a function of the generalized coordinates q_i and their temporal derivatives $\dot{q}_i$ (and also possibly of time t).

Let us take the total time derivative of the Lagrangian:

$$\frac{dL}{dt} = \sum_i \left(\frac{\partial L}{\partial q_i} \dot{q}_i + \frac{\partial L}{\partial \dot{q}_i} \ddot{q}_i \right) + \frac{\partial L}{\partial t}.$$

Using the Euler–Lagrange equations (6.9) and (7.2), we can rewrite this as

$$\frac{dL}{dt} = \sum_i (\dot{p}_i \dot{q}_i + p_i \ddot{q}_i) + \frac{\partial L}{\partial t}$$

$$= \frac{d}{dt} \sum_i (p_i \dot{q}_i) + \frac{\partial L}{\partial t},$$

and from the very definition (7.3) of the Hamiltonian, we obtain

$$\boxed{\frac{dH}{dt} = -\frac{\partial L}{\partial t}.} \tag{7.4}$$

This is an important equation, since it implies that if the Lagrangian does not depend explicitly on time, then the Hamiltonian function is conserved over time: it can be identified with the *conserved energy* of the system.

Returning to the Lagrangian, we have

$$dL = \sum_i \frac{\partial L}{\partial q_i} dq_i + \sum_i \frac{\partial L}{\partial \dot{q}_i} d\dot{q}_i + \frac{\partial L}{\partial t} dt$$

$$= \sum_i \dot{p}_i \, dq_i + \sum_i p_i \, d\dot{q}_i + \frac{\partial L}{\partial t} dt, \tag{7.5}$$

and thus, according to the definition (7.3) of the Hamiltonian,

$$dH = \sum_i p_i \, d\dot{q}_i + \sum_i \dot{q}_i \, dp_i - dL$$

$$= -\sum_i \dot{p}_i \, dq_i + \sum_i \dot{q}_i \, dp_i - \frac{\partial L}{\partial t} dt. \tag{7.6}$$

On the other hand, quite generally,

$$dH = \sum_i \frac{\partial H}{\partial q_i} dq_i + \sum_i \frac{\partial H}{\partial p_i} dp_i + \frac{\partial H}{\partial t} dt, \tag{7.7}$$

and comparing with Eq. (7.6), we obtain the Hamilton equations of motion

$$\dot{q}_i = \frac{\partial H}{\partial p_i}, \quad \dot{p}_i = -\frac{\partial H}{\partial q_i}, \tag{7.8}$$

together with

$$\frac{\partial H}{\partial t} = \frac{dH}{dt}, \tag{7.9}$$

implying that the Hamiltonian is conserved if it does not depend explicitly on time in accordance with (7.4).

7.2. Special cases

In most cases of interest, the Lagrangian is of the particular form

$$L = \frac{1}{2} \sum_{m,n} a_{mn}(q_i)\dot{q}_m\dot{q}_n - U(q_i), \tag{7.10}$$

where $a_{mn}(q_i)$ is a 3×3 matrix. Therefore,

$$p_i = \sum_n a_{in}\dot{q}_n,$$

and it follows that the Hamiltonian is of the form

$$H = \frac{1}{2} \sum_{m,n} a_{mn}^{-1}(q_i)p_m p_n + U(q_i), \tag{7.11}$$

where a_{mn}^{-1} is the inverse of the matrix a_{mn} (which is, fortunately, diagonal in most practical cases).

Let us work out some examples of Hamiltonian functions in various standard coordinate systems.

7.2.1. *Special coordinates*

In **Cartesian coordinates**, the generalized momenta are simply

$$\mathbf{p} = m\dot{\mathbf{x}},$$

and the Hamiltonian is

$$H = \frac{p^2}{2m} + U(\mathbf{x}). \tag{7.12}$$

In **cylindrical coordinates** (ρ, ϕ, z), the line element is

$$ds^2 = d\rho^2 + \rho^2 \, d\phi^2 + dz^2, \tag{7.13}$$

and therefore, the Lagrangian is

$$L = \frac{m}{2}(\dot\rho^2 + \rho^2\dot\phi^2 + \dot z^2) - U(\rho, \phi, z), \tag{7.14}$$

The generalized momenta are thus

$$p_\rho = m\dot\rho, \quad p_\phi = m\rho^2\dot\phi, \quad p_z = m\dot z,$$

and the Hamiltonian is

$$H = \frac{1}{2m}\left(p_\rho^2 + \frac{p_\phi^2}{\rho^2} + p_z^2\right) + U(\rho, \phi, z). \tag{7.15}$$

If the potential does not depend on ϕ, then p_ϕ is the conserved component of the angular momentum.

In **spherical coordinates** (r, θ, ϕ), the Lagrangian is

$$L = \frac{m}{2}(\dot r^2 + r^2\dot\theta^2 + r^2 \sin^2\theta \, \dot\phi^2) - U(r, \theta, \phi), \tag{7.16}$$

and the generalized momenta are thus

$$p_r = m\dot r, \quad p_\theta = mr^2\dot\theta, \quad p_\phi = mr^2 \sin^2\theta \, \dot\phi.$$

The Hamiltonian is

$$H = \frac{1}{2m}\left(p_r^2 + \frac{p_\theta^2}{r^2} + \frac{p_\phi^2}{r^2 \sin^2\theta}\right) + U(r, \theta, \phi). \tag{7.17}$$

Again, if the potential does not depend on ϕ, then p_ϕ is the conserved component of the angular momentum.

The Hamiltonian in **oblate** and **prolate** coordinates are given in Appendix B.

7.2.2. Relativistic Hamiltonian

In **special relativity**, the Lagrangian of a free particle with velocity **v** is

$$L = -mc^2\sqrt{1 - v^2/c^2}, \tag{7.18}$$

where c is the velocity of light. This is an example of a Lagrangian that is not of the form (7.10). For non-relativistic velocities, $v \ll c$, L reduces to the classical kinetic energy $mv^2/2$ plus an irrelevant additional constant term $-mc^2$ that does not affect the equations of motion. With some straightforward algebra, the Hamiltonian turns out to be

$$H = \sqrt{p^2c^2 + m^2c^4}, \tag{7.19}$$

with

$$\mathbf{p} = \frac{m\mathbf{v}}{\sqrt{1 - v^2/c^2}}$$

as the generalized momentum. For a particle at rest, $H = mc^2$.

In the presence of a Coulomb-like term α/r^2 (positive or negative charge), the Hamiltonian is

$$H = \sqrt{p^2c^2 + m^2c^4} + \frac{\alpha}{r}. \tag{7.20}$$

7.3. The action function

In Section 6.2 of Chapter 6, we defined the action as a functional, that is, a quantity that depends on functions. In the Lagrangian formalism, it is a functional of all the possible trajectories leading from one particular point at time t_1 to another particular point at time t_2. As we saw, among this countless trajectories, the only physical one is the trajectory for which the action is an extremum, a trajectory that follows from the Euler–Lagrange equations.

Let us now consider another kind of action, again an integral

$$S = \int L\, dt,$$

but involving *only* physical trajectories, starting from a fixed point at t_1 and ending at t_2 at *all the possible points* that can be reached with

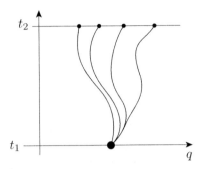

Fig. 7.1. The action as function of physical trajectories.

physically possible trajectories. Such an action is not a functional but a function of the end-point coordinates $q_i(t_2)$. The difference between the action as a functional and the action as a function of the possible final coordinates q_i at $t = t_2$ can be seen comparing Fig. 7.1 with Fig. 6.3 of Chapter 6.

Let us first consider a problem with one degree of freedom (the generalization to many degrees is obvious enough). According to the previous definition and the treatment in Section 6.2 of Chapter 6 (see particularly (6.13)), the variation of the action function S with respect to the coordinate is

$$\delta S = \left[\frac{\partial L}{\partial \dot{q}}\delta q\right]_{t_1}^{t_2} + \int_{t_1}^{t_2} \left(\frac{\partial L}{\partial q} - \frac{d}{dt}\left(\frac{\partial L}{\partial \dot{q}}\right)\right) dt. \tag{7.21}$$

The last term in this expression vanishes since we are considering only physical trajectories satisfying precisely the Euler–Lagrange equation. As for the first term, $\delta q(t_1) = 0$ and $\delta q(t_2)$ is simply δq. Accordingly, since $p = \partial L/\partial \dot{q}$, the above equation implies

$$\delta S = p\,\delta q.$$

Clearly, the generalization to any number of degrees of freedom is

$$\delta S = \sum_i p_i\,\delta q_i, \tag{7.22}$$

which in turn implies the important relation

$$\frac{\partial S}{\partial q_i} = p_i. \tag{7.23}$$

We can also consider one single physical trajectory starting at time t_1 and ending at a general time t or $t + dt$. From the very definition of S, we have

$$\frac{dS}{dt} = L,$$

and since

$$\frac{dS}{dt} = \frac{\partial S}{\partial t} + \sum_i \frac{\partial S}{\partial q_i} \dot{q}_i = \frac{\partial S}{\partial t} + \sum_i p_i \dot{q}_i \tag{7.24}$$

(using (7.23)), it also follows from the definition of the Hamiltonian H that

$$\frac{\partial S}{\partial t} + H = 0. \tag{7.25}$$

Actually, (7.24) can also be obtained directly from

$$dS = L \, dt = \sum_i p_i \, dq_i - H \, dt. \tag{7.26}$$

Now, quite generally, S and H are functions of q_i, but H is also a function of p_i. In order to have only q_i variables, we can use the relation (7.23) and write Eq. (7.25) in the form

$$\boxed{\frac{\partial S}{\partial t}(q_i, t) + H\left(q_i, \frac{\partial S}{\partial q_i}, t\right) = 0.} \tag{7.27}$$

This is the **Hamilton–Jacobi equation**, an equation for the action function in terms of a given Hamiltonian. It is the core of the Hamiltonian formulation of mechanics. It follows from the concept of canonical transformations, as we will now see. Some illustrative examples will be given afterwards.

7.4. Canonical transformations

In Hamilton's formalism, the equations of motion have the forms
(7.8). However, it is always possible to perform a change of coordinates from the old coordinates q_i and p_i to some new coordinates

$$Q_j(q_i, p_i, t), \quad P_j(q_i, p_i, t),$$

without altering the physical properties of the system to be described.
All we need is that the Hamilton equations (7.8) take the new forms

$$\dot{Q}_i = \frac{\partial H'}{\partial P_i}, \quad \dot{P}_i = -\frac{\partial H'}{\partial Q_i},$$

where $H'(P_i, Q_i, t)$ is the new Hamiltonian. Such coordinate transformations are called **canonical transformations**. The idea is
that in these new coordinates, the Hamilton equations take a form
particularly simple. Let us see how to proceed.

The problem, then, is to find the way to change to new coordinates
and a new H'. For this purpose, we note that the conditions for
the action functionals to be extremal are, in both old and new
coordinates,

$$\delta S = \int \left(\sum_i p_i \, dq_i - H \, dt \right) = 0$$

and

$$\delta S = \int \left(\sum_i P_i \, dQ_i - H' \, dt \right) = 0.$$

Since the difference between these two integrals is also zero, we can
conclude that the difference between their integrands must be the
differential dF of a certain function F (because $\delta \int dF = 0$). Such a
function is called a **generating function**. Thus,

$$dF = \sum_i p_i \, dq_i - \sum_i P_i \, dQ_i + (H' - H)dt. \tag{7.28}$$

Suppose now, in particular, that $F(q_i, Q_i, t)$ is defined as a function
of the old and new coordinates, q_i and Q_i, respectively. In this case,

Eq. (7.28) implies

$$p_i = \frac{\partial F}{\partial q_i}, \quad P_i = -\frac{\partial F}{\partial Q_i}, \quad H' = H + \frac{\partial F}{\partial t}. \qquad (7.29)$$

Yet another possibility is to use, instead of $F(q_i, Q_i, t)$, a generating function $F_2(q_i, P_i, t)$ related to the previous one by

$$F_2 = F + \sum_i P_i Q_i,$$

in which case

$$dF_2 = \sum_i p_i \, dq_i + \sum_i Q_i \, dP_i + (H' - H)dt,$$

and accordingly,

$$p_i = \frac{\partial F_2}{\partial q_i}, \quad Q_i = \frac{\partial F_2}{\partial P_i}, \quad H' = H + \frac{\partial F_2}{\partial t}. \qquad (7.30)$$

Some other possibilities are $F_3(p_i, Q_i, t)$ and $F_4(p_i, P_i, t)$, but we will not consider them in this text.

We thus see that it is possible to change the form of the Hamiltonian by a canonical transformation. Now, the obvious question is: What is the simplest possible Hamiltonian? Clearly, a zero Hamiltonian $H' = 0$, since the Hamilton equations would be trivially satisfied. Of course, the problem is to find the appropriate canonical transformation, but this may be somewhat easier in many cases.

So, let us see how to ensure that $H' = 0$. According to (7.29), we need

$$H + \frac{\partial F}{\partial t} = 0, \qquad (7.31)$$

but this is precisely the Hamilton–Jacobi equation (7.27) with the action function S as the generating function! More precisely,

$$\frac{\partial S}{\partial t} + H(q_i, p_i, t) = 0, \qquad (7.32)$$

with $p_i = \partial S/\partial q_i$ in accordance with (7.29). Then, with $H' = 0$, the Hamilton equations (7.8) have the trivial solutions

$$P_i = \text{constant}, \quad Q_i = \text{constant}. \qquad (7.33)$$

In practice, one can take all the constants of integration appearing in the solution for S as the coordinates Q_i and then derive S with respect to these "constants", as if they were variables, thus obtaining new constants P_i in accordance with (7.29). That is,

$$P_i = \frac{\partial S}{\partial Q_i} = \text{constant}. \tag{7.34}$$

Summing up, we have reduced the problem to solving the Hamilton–Jacobi equation or, more precisely, to finding one particular solution of it. The procedure will be illustrated in the following section.

7.5. Examples

There is no general procedure for solving the Hamilton–Jacobi equation, but in many practical cases, it can be solved by separation of variables. An important case is that of a Hamiltonian that does not depend explicitly on time. In this case, we can set

$$S(q_i, t) = Q_t t + \bar{S}(q_i), \tag{7.35}$$

where Q_t is a constant that can be interpreted as a new coordinate. Thus, the HJ equation reduces to

$$H\left(q_i, \frac{\partial \bar{S}}{\partial q_i}\right) = -Q_t = E, \tag{7.36}$$

identifying $-Q_t$ as the conserved energy E. Then

$$P_t = \frac{\partial \bar{S}}{\partial Q_t} = -\frac{\partial \bar{S}}{\partial E}$$

is another constant of motion.

Another possibility is that one or more coordinates be *cyclic*, that is, the Hamiltonian does not depend explicitly on them. For instance, it does not depend on the ϕ coordinate in a rotationally symmetric problem. In this case, the action function can be written as

$$S(q_i, \phi, t) = p_\phi \phi + S(q_i, t), \tag{7.37}$$

where p_ϕ is the conserved angular momentum and q_i are all the remaining coordinates.

Let us illustrate the procedure with a typical problem.

7.5.1. *Potential with dipole term*

Consider a particle of mass m in a potential field

$$V(r, \theta) = -\frac{a}{r} + mp\frac{\cos\theta}{r^2}$$

in spherical coordinates, with a and p constants. The second term corresponds to a dipole correction to the radial potential (see Section 2.3 and (6.18)).

The Hamiltonian for this problem is given by (7.17):

$$H = \frac{1}{2m}\left(p_r^2 + \frac{p_\theta^2}{r^2} + \frac{p_\phi^2}{r^2\sin^2\theta}\right) + V(r, \theta). \tag{7.38}$$

Then, with (7.35) and (7.36), the Hamilton–Jacobi equation can be written in the form

$$E = \frac{1}{2m}\left(\frac{\partial\bar{S}}{\partial r}\right)^2 - \frac{a}{r} + \frac{1}{2mr^2}\left[\left(\frac{\partial\bar{S}}{\partial\theta}\right)^2 + 2m^2p\cos\theta\right]$$

$$+ \frac{1}{2mr^2\sin^2\theta}\left(\frac{\partial\bar{S}}{\partial\phi}\right)^2. \tag{7.39}$$

The important point is that this equation can be solved by the separation of variables:

$$\bar{S}(r, \theta, \phi) = S_r(r) + S_\theta(\theta) + S_\phi(\phi). \tag{7.40}$$

Noticing that ϕ is a cyclic coordinate and therefore $S_\phi(\phi) = Q_\phi\phi$, we get the two decoupled equations:

$$E = \frac{1}{2m}\left(\frac{dS_r}{dr}\right)^2 - \frac{a}{r} + \frac{Q_\theta^2}{2mr^2}, \tag{7.41}$$

$$Q_\theta^2 = \left(\frac{dS_\theta}{d\theta}\right)^2 + 2m^2p\cos\theta + \frac{Q_\phi^2}{\sin^2\theta}, \tag{7.42}$$

where Q_θ is a separation constant. Also note that $Q_\phi = p_\phi = \partial S_\phi/\partial\phi = L$ is just the conserved angular momentum.

Summing up, the calculation of S is reduced to the calculation of two quadratures:

$$S = -Et + p_\phi \phi + \int \sqrt{Q_\theta - 2m^2 p \cos\theta - p_\phi^2/\sin^2\theta}\, d\theta$$

$$+ \int \sqrt{2m(E + a/r) - Q_\theta/r^2}\, dr, \tag{7.43}$$

where the constants of integration are E, Q_θ and p_ϕ. The solutions of the equations of motion follow from the conjugate coordinates P_i. Thus, $\partial S/\partial E = P_E = \text{constant}$ (according to (7.34)) implies

$$t = \int \frac{m\, dr}{[2m(E + a/r) - Q_\theta/r^2]^{1/2}}, \tag{7.44}$$

relating r with time t. Furthermore, $P_\phi = \partial S/\partial p_\phi$ is also a constant, and thus (again according to (7.34)),

$$\phi = \int \frac{p_\phi\, d\theta}{\sin^2\theta[Q_\theta - 2m^2 p\cos\theta - p_\phi^2/\sin^2\theta]^{1/2}}, \tag{7.45}$$

which gives the form of the orbit in terms of the constant angular momentum $p_\phi \equiv L$.

Writing (7.42) as

$$Q_\theta^2 = p_\theta^2 + 2m^2 p\cos\theta + \frac{p_\phi^2}{\sin^2\theta}, \tag{7.46}$$

the energy (or Hamiltonian) turns out to be

$$E = \frac{p_r^2}{2m} + \frac{Q_\theta^2}{2mr^2} - \frac{a}{r}, \tag{7.47}$$

thus relating Q_θ to the energy.

The Kepler problem is recovered if $a = GMm$ and $p = 0$ (no dipole term). Then $Q_\theta \to L^2/2m$, $Q_\phi = L$, and $\theta = \pi/2$ all the time. If the dipole term is present, the particle cannot stay in the $\theta = \pi/2$ plane because there is a force in the θ direction (see Section 2.3 of Chapter 2); in this case, there is an additional constant of motion Q_θ, related to the conserved energy, besides the angular momentum $p_\phi = L$. Choosing the values of p_ϕ and Q_θ according to the initial conditions, the last two integrals give the trajectory of a particle as $t = t(r)$ and $\phi = \phi(\theta)$ (numerical integration is necessary). For an approximate solution, see Section 6.3.2 of Chapter 6.

7.6. Action-angle variables

An important physical situation is one in which the motion of a system is periodic, that is, some of its parameters return to the same values after a certain finite time. In some problems, however, to find the period itself may be of more interest than finding the actual motion. In such cases, the so-called technique of action-angle variables is most useful.

7.6.1. *One degree of freedom*

Let us first start with a one-dimensional problem in order to fix the ideas. Define the *action variable*

$$J = \oint q \, dp \qquad (7.48)$$

as the integral in phase space carried over one complete period. For a conservative system,

$$H(p, q) = E,$$

and this equation can be inverted in order to get

$$q = q(p, E).$$

Therefore, after the integral (7.48) is carried out, there remains only $J = J(E)$ or, equivalently,

$$H = H(J), \qquad (7.49)$$

and the Hamiltonian depends only on J.

We can now perform a canonical transformation taking the action function as a generating function of the form $F_2(q, P)$, as in (7.30), with J as the new momentum. From

$$F_2 = S(q, J),$$

it follows, according to the second equation in (7.30), the new generalized coordinate (we call it ϕ instead of Q) is

$$\phi = \frac{\partial S}{\partial J}.$$

Furthermore, since $F_2 = S$ does not depend on time, the Hamiltonian remains constant.

The equations of motion are thus

$$\dot{J} = -\frac{\partial H(J)}{\partial \phi} = 0, \quad \dot{\phi} = \frac{\partial H(J)}{\partial J} = \nu(J), \tag{7.50}$$

where ν is a constant that depends only on J, which is also a constant. The second equation can be trivially solved:

$$\phi = \nu t + \phi_0.$$

Thus, the constant ν can be identified with the frequency of the system, as in the following example.

Consider as an illustrative (and almost trivial) example a one-dimensional harmonic oscillator. Its trajectory in phase space is an ellipse, given by (1.8), with axes $\sqrt{2mE}$ and $\sqrt{2E/m\omega^2}$. The area of this ellipse is thus

$$J = 2\pi E/\omega.$$

The Hamiltonian in terms of J is

$$H = \frac{\omega}{2\pi} J,$$

and therefore, according to (7.50), the frequency of oscillations is indeed $\nu = \omega/2\pi$, as we already knew!

7.6.2. *Multiple degrees of freedom*

Let us now consider the case of N degrees of freedom. Suppose that the Hamilton–Jacobi equation admits a complete separation of variables, as in the cases previously studied, and also that the problem is time-independent. This means that it admits a solution of the form

$$S(q_1, q_2, \ldots, q_N, t) = -Et + \sum_i S_i(q_i), \qquad (7.51)$$

and that there are N constants of integration: the energy E and another $N - 1$ constants. For instance, in the Kepler problem in a two-dimensional plane, we have E and the component L_z of the angular momentum as the two constants of motion, and for the three-dimensional problem of the dipole, we have three constants of motion: E, p_ϕ and Q_θ. In conclusion, we can set $S_i(q_i; \alpha_1, \alpha_2, \ldots, \alpha_N)$, with $\alpha_1 = E$.

According to (7.30),

$$p_i = \frac{\partial S}{\partial q_i} = \frac{d}{dq_i} S_i(q_i; \alpha_1, \alpha_2, \ldots, \alpha_N), \qquad (7.52)$$

implying that $p_i = p_i(q_i; \alpha_1, \alpha_2, \ldots, \alpha_N)$, a relation which can be inverted[2] in order to get

$$q_i = q_i(p_i; \alpha_1, \alpha_2, \ldots, \alpha_N).$$

Now, for a conservative system,

$$H(p_i, q_i) = E = \alpha_1,$$

and this implies that the Hamiltonian is a function of the set α_i only:

$$H(\alpha_1, \alpha_2, \ldots, \alpha_N).$$

We can now define

$$J_i = \oint p_i \, dq_i \qquad (7.53)$$

for each of the N coordinates. After these integrals are carried out, there remains N integrals $J_i = J_i(\alpha_1, \alpha_2, \ldots, \alpha_N)$ or equivalently

---

[2]That such an inversion is possible is almost always the case, except for some pathological cases that we will not consider here.

$\alpha_i = \alpha_i(J_1, J_2, \ldots, J_N)$. This implies that the Hamiltonian can also be taken as a function of the J_i's only:

$$H = H(J_1, J_2, \ldots, J_N),$$

and similarly the action functions $S_i(q_i; J_1, J_2, \ldots, J_N)$.

We can now perform a canonical transformation, as in the case of only one degree of freedom. Defining conjugate variables

$$\phi_i = \sum_i \frac{\partial S_i(q_i; J_1, J_2, \ldots, J_N)}{\partial J_i}, \tag{7.54}$$

the equations of motion turn out to be

$$\dot{J}_i = -\frac{\partial H(J_1, J_2, \ldots, J_N)}{\partial \phi_i} = 0, \quad \dot{\phi}_i = \frac{\partial H(J_1, J_2, \ldots, J_N)}{\partial J_i}$$

$$= \nu_i(J_1, J_2, \ldots, J_N),$$

where ν_i are constants that depend only of the J_i's, which are also constants. The second equation can be trivially solved:

$$\phi_i = \nu_i t + \phi_{i0}.$$

This identifies ν_i as the frequencies of the system.

Let us clarify the whole procedure with a couple of illustrative problems.

7.6.3. *The Kepler problem again*

As an illustrative example, let us consider the Kepler problem again, starting from the Lagrangian

$$\mathcal{L} = \frac{m}{2}(\dot{r}^2 + r^2\dot{\phi}^2) + \frac{GMm}{r}$$

(in obvious notation). The generalized momenta are

$$p_r = m\dot{r}, \quad p_\phi = mr^2\dot{\phi},$$

and the Hamiltonian is

$$H = \frac{1}{2m}\left(p_r^2 + \frac{p_\phi^2}{r^2}\right) - \frac{GMm}{r}. \tag{7.55}$$

As a two-dimensional problem, it admits two constants of motion: the energy $E = H$ and the angular momentum $L = p_\phi$ (not to be confused with the Lagrangian $\mathcal{L}$). We assume the motion of the particle to be bounded, that is to say $E < 0$.

We now calculate the action variables. The first one is trivial:

$$J_\phi = \oint p_\phi \, d\phi = 2\pi L,$$

since $p_\phi = L$ is constant. The second action variable (which is not so trivial) is the integral of p_r (as given by (7.55) with $H = E$), that is,

$$J_r = 2 \int_{r_{\min}}^{r_{\max}} p_r \, dr = 2 \int_{r_{\min}}^{r_{\max}} \sqrt{-L^2 + 2GMm^2 r - 2m|E|r^2} \, \frac{dr}{r},$$
$$(7.56)$$

where $r_{\min}$ and $r_{\max}$ are the minimum and maximum values of r (that is, the perihelion and the aphelion) and the factor 2 includes the complete cycle between them.

In order to solve the integral (7.56), we note that $r_{\min}$ and $r_{\max}$ are the two roots of the term in the square root. Therefore, the integral is of the form

$$J_r = 2\sqrt{2m|E|} \int_a^b \sqrt{b-r}\sqrt{r-a}\, \frac{dr}{r}, \qquad (7.57)$$

where

$$a + b = \frac{GMm}{|E|}, \qquad ab = \frac{L^2}{2m|E|}. \qquad (7.58)$$

This last integral can be solved by standard methods. For our present purpose, it is enough to use the formula[3]

$$\int_a^b \sqrt{b-r}\sqrt{r-a}\, \frac{dr}{r} = \frac{\pi}{2}(a + b - 2\sqrt{ab}), \qquad (7.59)$$

from where it follows

$$J_r = 2\pi\left(-L + GMm\sqrt{\frac{m}{2|E|}}\right). \qquad (7.60)$$

---

[3]Redefine $2r = a + b - (b - a)\sin x$ and you get formula 3.613.2 of Gradshteyn and Rizhik *Tables of Integrals, Series, and Products* (Academic Press, 2007).

Summing up, we obtain a formula for the energy as a function of the two action variables J_ϕ and J_r:

$$E = -2\pi^2 \frac{(GM)^2 m^3}{(J_\phi + J_r)^2}. \tag{7.61}$$

The frequency of the system can now be obtained, taking the derivative of E with respect to either J_ϕ or J_r: The result is

$$\nu = 4\pi^2 \frac{(GM)^2 m^3}{(J_\phi + J_r)^3} \tag{7.62}$$

or, substituting the values of J_r and J_ϕ in terms of the energy,

$$\nu = \frac{1}{2\pi GM} \left(\frac{2|E|}{m} \right)^{3/2}, \tag{7.63}$$

which is Kepler's third law: compare with (2.25).

The fact that the energy depends on the term $J_\phi + J_r$ and not on J_ϕ and J_r separately implies that the two frequencies coincide. Such a situation is called *degenerate*. In the Kepler problem, the periods of oscillation in the radial and angular directions coincide and, as a consequence, the orbits are closed.[4]

7.6.4. *Kepler problem with a correction*

Let us consider a spherically symmetric potential of the Kepler type with a small correction $\propto r^{-2}$, namely a potential of the form

$$V = -\frac{K}{r} - \frac{\epsilon}{r^2}.$$

The Lagrangian is

$$\mathcal{L} = \frac{m}{2}(\dot{r}^2 + r^2 \dot{\phi}^2) + \frac{K}{r} + \frac{\epsilon}{r^2},$$

and the Hamiltonian is

$$H = \frac{1}{2m}\left(p_r^2 + \frac{p_\phi^2}{r^2} \right) - \frac{K}{r} - \frac{\epsilon}{r^2}.$$

---

[4]This is also the reason for the existence of an additional constant of motion: the Runge–Lenz vector mentioned in Section 2.2.1 of Chapter 2.

There are two conserved quantities, the energy and the angular momentum:

$$E = H, \quad p_\phi = L = mr^2\dot{\phi},$$

and we also have the generalized momentum

$$p_r^2 = 2m\left(E + \frac{K}{r} + \frac{\epsilon}{r^2}\right) - \frac{L^2}{r^2},$$

together with the equation of motion

$$m\ddot{r} = -\frac{K}{r^2} + (L^2 - 2m\epsilon)\frac{1}{mr^3}.$$

We see that we have the same equations as in the previous (standard) Kepler problem, with only the substitutions $L^2 \to L^2 - 2m\epsilon$ and $GMm \to K$. (Actually, these are the equations of motion of a charged particle in a Coulomb field taking relativistic effects into account, but that is outside the scope of this book.[5])

Thus, we can use Eq. (7.61) with the appropriate substitution and obtain

$$E = -2\pi^2 \frac{(GM)^2 m^3}{((J_\phi^2 - 2m\epsilon)^{1/2} + J_r)^2}. \tag{7.64}$$

Taking derivatives of the energy with respect to J_r and J_ϕ, respectively, we obtain two frequencies of oscillations:

$$\nu_r = \frac{m}{2\pi K}\left(\frac{2|E|}{m}\right)^{3/2} \tag{7.65}$$

in the radial direction and

$$\nu_\phi = \frac{1}{(1 - 2m\epsilon/L^2)^{1/2}}\nu_r \tag{7.66}$$

in the azimuthal direction. Unlike the case of the standard Kepler problem, the two frequencies do not coincide. This fact implies that, for bounded orbits, the correction term produces a perihelion shift and the orbits are not closed.

---

[5]See, e.g., Landau and Lifshitz (1971) Theory of Fields. Section 39.

Chapter 8

Variational Problems

Having learned how to minimize a functional such as the action, we can use the same procedure to solve a variety of problems. Let us work out three illustrative examples in the following sections.

8.1. The brachistochrone

A particle slides without friction from a point A to a lower point B along a fixed curved, as in Fig. 8.1. Let us find the curve for which the time of descent is minimum (such a curve is called *brachistochrone* from Greek *brakistos*, shortest, and *kronos*, time).

Let the coordinates of the upper point A be $(0, y_0)$, and let a trajectory from A to B be the curve $x = x(y)$ (see Fig. 8.1). Then the (squared) velocity along such a curve is

$$v^2 = \dot{x}^2 + \dot{y}^2 = ((x')^2 + 1)\dot{y}^2,$$

where $x' = dx/dy$. Accordingly, if the particle is initially at rest at the point A, the conservation of total energy implies

$$\frac{1}{2}((x')^2 + 1)\dot{y}^2 - g(y_0 - y) = 0. \tag{8.1}$$

Solving for t, the time taken to descent turns out to be

$$t = \int_{y_0}^{0} dy \sqrt{\frac{(x')^2 + 1}{2g(y_0 - y)}} \tag{8.2}$$

in accordance with (1.4).

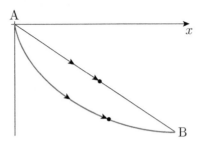

Fig. 8.1. Brachistochrone.

Now, compare this last formula with (6.10) and identify

$$\sqrt{\frac{(x')^2 + 1}{2g(y_0 - y)}} \to L,$$

as the "Lagrangian", together with the changes

$$y \to t, \quad x \to q, \quad x' \to \dot{q}.$$

Then, with the appropriate substitutions, the time of descent, given by (8.2), is minimum for a trajectory $x(y)$ satisfying the Euler–Lagrange equation

$$\frac{\partial L}{\partial x} - \frac{d}{dy}\left(\frac{\partial L}{\partial x'}\right) = 0. \tag{8.3}$$

This can be integrated immediately since $\partial L/\partial x = 0$, with the result

$$\frac{\partial L}{\partial x'} = \frac{x'}{\sqrt{2g[(x')^2 + 1](y_0 - y)}} = K, \tag{8.4}$$

where K is a constant. It is easy to check by direct substitution that the curve defined by

$$x = R(\theta - \sin\theta),$$
$$y = R(1 + \cos\theta) \tag{8.5}$$

(and thus $x' = -(1 - \cos\theta)/\sin\theta$) satisfies Eq. (8.4) if $K = -1/\sqrt{2R}$. With $y_0 = 2R$, this is precisely the equation of a cycloid, with parameter θ, which we already covered in Section 1.2.6 of Chapter 1.

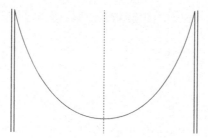

Fig. 8.2. Hanging rope: catenary.

The initial point A corresponds to $\theta = 0$, and the final point B is any point on the cycloid. A particle sliding from point A along a cycloid will reach the lower point B in the shortest time as compared with any other descent curve.

8.2. The hanging rope

What is the shape of a rope of uniform density hanging from two fixed points? To solve this problem, it is enough to note that the shape, given as $y = y(x)$ or $x = x(y)$ in Fig. 8.2, must be such that the potential energy of the rope is the minimum possible; otherwise, the rope would look for an even lower energy configuration. Let us take, for simplicity, the two hanging points to be at the same horizontal level with a separation $2a$.

Since the potential energy of a segment of the rope of length ds is $\sigma y\, ds$, where σ is the mass density per unit length, the potential energy is then

$$\int_{-a}^{a} g\sigma y\, ds = \int_{-a}^{a} g\sigma y\sqrt{1 + (dy/dx)^2}\, dx,$$

where $ds = \sqrt{dx^2 + dy^2}$ is the differential length along the rope. Furthermore, it must be taken into account that the total length l of the rope is constant, which implies a constraint

$$l = \int_{-a}^{a} ds = \int_{-a}^{a} \sqrt{1 + (dy/dx)^2}\, dx.$$

We must therefore minimize the "action"

$$\int_{-a}^{a} [(g\sigma y\sqrt{1+(y')^2}\,dx + \lambda\sqrt{1+(y')^2}\,dx]$$

$$= \int_{-a}^{a} [(g\sigma y + \lambda)\sqrt{1+(y')^2}]dx, \qquad (8.6)$$

where $y' = dy/dx$, and we have included a term with a Lagrange multiplier λ to ensure that the length of the rope is taken as fixed. The above integral is the quantity that must be minimized. Accordingly, we can identify the term in square brackets as the "Lagrangian" L, with

$$t \to x$$

and

$$\dot{y} \to dy/dx = y',$$

and the "momentum" that turns out to be

$$p = \frac{\partial L}{\partial y'} = \frac{g\sigma y + \lambda}{\sqrt{1+(y')^2}}y'.$$

It is now convenient to define a "Hamiltonian" that is constant because the "Lagrangian" does not depend on the "time" x. Explicitly, the conserved "energy" is (instead of $H = p\dot{y} - L$)

$$E = py' - L = \frac{(g\sigma y + \lambda)}{\sqrt{1+(y')^2}}. \qquad (8.7)$$

Solving for the y' term, we find the equation

$$y' = \frac{dy}{dx} = \sqrt{\left(\frac{g\sigma y + \lambda}{E}\right)^2 - 1},$$

with solution

$$g\sigma y + \lambda = E\cosh(g\sigma x/E). \qquad (8.8)$$

If $x = y = 0$ is the lowest point of the rope, then $\lambda = E$. Furthermore, if it is hanging from a height y_0 at $x = \pm a$, then

$$g\sigma y_0 = E[\cosh(g\sigma a/E) - 1],$$

giving E as a function of the parameters a, y_0 and σ.

The resulting curve is a hyperbolic cosine, also called a *catenary*, from Latin *catena*, chain, since it is the figure of a hanging chain.

8.3. Minimal surfaces

The *Plateau problem* is to find a surface with the minimum area limited by some given boundaries, namely closed curves.[1] The problem has given rise to a whole branch of mathematics, but for our present purpose, it is enough to consider its most simple version: to find the minimal surface bounded by two parallel rings of equal radius, as shown in Fig. 8.3.

Given the axial symmetry of the configuration, the solution must be a surface of revolution generated by the curve $r = f(z)$ (in cylindrical coordinates). The area of such a surface is

$$A = 2\pi \int_{-L}^{L} f(z)\sqrt{1 + (f'(z))^2}\, dz, \tag{8.9}$$

Fig. 8.3. Minimal surface between two rings.

---

[1]Named after Joseph Plateau (1801–1883), Belgian physicist who experimented with soap films.

where $2L$ is the separation between the two parallel rings. This integral can be minimized interpreting the term

$$f(z)\sqrt{1 + (f'(z))^2}$$

as a Lagrangian, with $f(z)$ the generalized coordinate and z the "time" coordinate. The Euler–Lagrange equation takes the form

$$\frac{d}{dz}\left[\frac{ff'}{\sqrt{1 + f'^2}}\right] = \sqrt{1 + f'^2}. \tag{8.10}$$

It is easy to check by direct substitution that the solution of this equation is

$$f(z) = a\cosh(z/a), \tag{8.11}$$

where a is a constant with the dimension of length. The minimal surface is thus a "catenary of revolution" with a waist radius a, as seen in Fig. 8.3. The size of the waist is determined by the relation

$$R = a\cosh(L/a)$$

between the radius R of each ring and their separation $2L$.

Appendix A

Derivation of the Lagrange Equations

Let us start with (6.7). We obtain the following with some straightforward algebra:

$$\sum_{k=1}^{F} Q_k \delta q_k = \sum_{i=1}^{N} m_i \ddot{\mathbf{r}}_i \cdot \delta \mathbf{r}_i = \sum_{i=1}^{N} m_i \ddot{\mathbf{r}}_i \cdot \sum_{k=1}^{F} \frac{\partial \mathbf{r}_i}{\partial q_k} \delta q_k$$

$$= \sum_{k=1}^{F} \left(\sum_{i=1}^{N} m_i \ddot{\mathbf{r}}_i \cdot \frac{\partial \mathbf{r}_i}{\partial q_k} \right) \delta q_k. \tag{A.1}$$

At this point, we need some useful results to proceed. First, note that, since $\mathbf{r_i} = \mathbf{r_i}(q_1, q_2, \ldots, q_F, t)$,

$$\dot{\mathbf{r}}_i = \frac{\partial \mathbf{r_i}}{\partial q_1} \dot{q}_1 + \frac{\partial \mathbf{r_i}}{\partial q_2} \dot{q}_2 + \cdots + \frac{\partial \mathbf{r_i}}{\partial q_F} \dot{q}_F + \frac{\partial \mathbf{r_i}}{\partial t}, \tag{A.2}$$

and therefore, if $\dot{q}_i$ is interpreted as a variable of the function $\dot{\mathbf{r}}_i(q_k, \dot{q}_k, t)$, then

$$\frac{\partial \dot{\mathbf{r_i}}}{\partial \dot{q}_k} = \frac{\partial \mathbf{r_i}}{\partial q_k} \tag{A.3}$$

(it is as if the "points" in the numerator and the denominator canceled each other out).

Another useful result is

$$\frac{d}{dt}\left(\frac{\partial \mathbf{r_i}}{\partial q_k}\right) = \frac{\partial}{\partial q_1}\left(\frac{\partial \mathbf{r_i}}{\partial q_k}\right)\dot{q}_1 + \frac{\partial}{\partial q_2}\left(\frac{\partial \mathbf{r_i}}{\partial q_k}\right)\dot{q}_2$$

$$+ \cdots + \frac{\partial}{\partial q_F}\left(\frac{\partial \mathbf{r_i}}{\partial q_k}\right)\dot{q}_F + \frac{\partial^2 \mathbf{r_i}}{\partial t \partial q_k},$$

and comparing this last equation with the derivative of (A.2) with respect to q_j, it turns out that

$$\frac{d}{dt}\left(\frac{\partial \mathbf{r_i}}{\partial q_k}\right) = \frac{\partial \dot{\mathbf{r}}_i}{\partial q_k}. \tag{A.4}$$

We are now ready to manipulate Eq. (A.1) and bring it to a useful form:

$$\sum_{k=1}^{F}\left(\sum_{i=1}^{N} m_i\ddot{\mathbf{r}}_i \cdot \frac{\partial \mathbf{r}_i}{\partial q_k}\right)\delta q_k$$

$$= \sum_{k=1}^{F}\left[\frac{d}{dt}\left(\sum_{i=1}^{N} m_i\dot{\mathbf{r}}_i \cdot \frac{\partial \mathbf{r}_i}{\partial q_k}\right) - \sum_{i=1}^{N} m_i\dot{\mathbf{r}}_i \cdot \frac{d}{dt}\left(\frac{\partial \mathbf{r}_i}{\partial q_k}\right)\right]\delta q_k$$

$$= \sum_{k=1}^{F}\left[\frac{d}{dt}\left(\sum_{i=1}^{N} m_i\dot{\mathbf{r}}_i \cdot \frac{\partial \dot{\mathbf{r}}_i}{\partial \dot{q}_k}\right) - \sum_{i=1}^{N} m_i\dot{\mathbf{r}}_i \cdot \frac{\partial \dot{\mathbf{r}}_i}{\partial q_i}\right]\delta q_k, \tag{A.5}$$

where use has been made in the last step of our results (A.3) and (A.4).

Then, according to (A.1),

$$\sum_{k=1}^{F} Q_k \delta q_k = \sum_{k=1}^{F}\left[\frac{d}{dt}\left(\frac{1}{2}\sum_{i=1}^{N} m_i\frac{\partial}{\partial \dot{q}_i}(\dot{\mathbf{r}}_i \cdot \dot{\mathbf{r}}_i)\right)\right.$$

$$\left. - \sum_{i=1}^{N}\frac{1}{2}m_i\frac{\partial}{\partial q_j}(\dot{\mathbf{r}}_i \cdot \dot{\mathbf{r}}_i)\right]\delta q_k$$

$$= \sum_{k=1}^{F}\left[\frac{d}{dt}\left(\frac{\partial}{\partial \dot{q}_i}T\right) - \frac{\partial}{\partial q_j}T\right]. \tag{A.6}$$

In this last step, the formula for the kinetic energy

$$T = \sum_{i=1}^{N}\frac{1}{2}m_i\dot{\mathbf{r}}_i \cdot \dot{\mathbf{r}}_i$$

has been used. With Eq. (A.6), the proof of (6.8) is completed.

Appendix B

Prolate and Oblate Coordinates

Prolate Spheroidal Coordinates (ξ, η, ϕ) are defined as

$$x = a\sqrt{(\xi^2 - 1)(1 - \eta^2)}\cos\phi,$$
$$y = a\sqrt{(\xi^2 - 1)(1 - \eta^2)}\sin\phi, \qquad (B.1)$$
$$z = a\xi\eta,$$

with $1 \leq \xi < \infty$ and $-1 \leq \eta \leq 1$, surfaces with ξ constant are ellipsoids with foci at $z = \pm a$, semi-major axis $a\xi$ and semi-minor axis $a\sqrt{1 - \xi^2}$, see Fig. B.1. If we define r_+ and r_- as the distances of an arbitrary point with coordinates (x, y, z) from each of the foci,

$$r_\pm = \sqrt{x^2 + y^2 + (z \mp a)^2},$$

then

$$r_\pm = a(\xi \mp \eta) \qquad (B.2)$$

or $\xi = (r_- + r_+)/2a$ and $\eta = (r_- - r_+)/2a$.

The line element is

$$ds^2 = a^2(\xi^2 - \eta^2)\left[\frac{d\xi^2}{\xi^2 - 1} + \frac{d\eta^2}{1 - \eta^2}\right] + a^2(\xi^2 - 1)(1 - \eta^2)d\phi^2.$$

The Lagrangian is

$$L = \frac{ma^2}{2} \left[(\xi^2 - \eta^2) \left(\frac{\dot{\xi}^2}{\xi^2 - 1} + \frac{\dot{\eta}^2}{1 - \eta^2} \right) \right.$$

$$\left. + (\xi^2 - 1)(1 - \eta^2)\dot{\phi}^2 \right] - U(\xi, \eta, \phi), \qquad \text{(B.3)}$$

and the Hamiltonian is

$$H = \frac{1}{2ma^2(\xi^2 - \eta^2)} \left[(\xi^2 - 1)p_\xi^2 + (1 - \eta^2)p_\eta^2 \right.$$

$$\left. + \left(\frac{1}{\xi^2 - 1} + \frac{1}{1 - \eta^2} \right) p_\phi^2 \right] + U(\xi, \eta, \phi). \qquad \text{(B.4)}$$

These coordinates can conveniently be used in the problem of a double potential, for instance, two fixed charges q_i located at $z = \pm a$ (see Fig. B.1). The potential is

$$V = \frac{q_1}{r_1} + \frac{q_2}{r_2}.$$

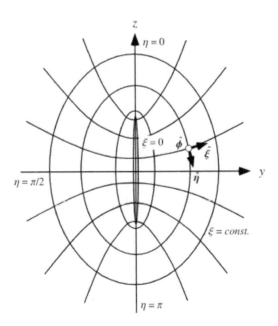

Fig. B.1.

This potential, according to (B.2) and some straightforward algebra, turns out to be

$$V = \frac{(q_1 + q_2)\xi + (q_1 - q_2)\eta}{a(\xi^2 - \eta^2)}. \tag{B.5}$$

It is then possible to perform a separation of variables to solve the corresponding HJ equation (see, e.g., Landau and Lifshitz, *Classical Mechanics*, where this problem is treated as an exercise in Section 48).

Oblate spheroidal coordinates (ξ, η, ϕ) are defined as

$$x = a \cosh \xi \cos \eta \cos \phi,$$
$$y = a \cosh \xi \cos \eta \sin \phi, \tag{B.6}$$
$$z = a \sinh \xi \sin \eta,$$

the line element is

$$ds^2 = a^2(\sinh^2 \xi + \sin^2 \eta)(d\xi^2 + d\eta^2) + a^2 \cosh^2 \xi \cos^2 \eta \, d\phi^2. \tag{B.7}$$

Surfaces of constant ξ are oblate (flattened) ellipsoids (Fig. B.2).

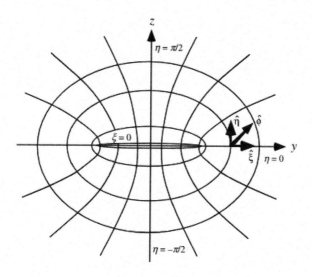

Fig. B.2.

Thus, the Lagrangian is

$$L = \frac{m}{2}[a^2(\sinh^2\xi + \sin^2\eta)(\dot{\xi}^2 + \dot{\eta}^2) + a^2\cosh^2\xi\cos^2\eta\,\dot{\phi}^2] - U(\xi, \eta, \phi),$$

(B.8)

the generalized momenta are

$$p_\xi = ma^2(\sinh^2\xi + \sin^2\eta)\dot{\xi},$$

$$p_\eta = ma^2(\sinh^2\xi + \sin^2\eta)\dot{\eta}, \quad \text{(B.9)}$$

$$p_\phi = ma^2\cosh^2\xi\cos^2\eta\,\dot{\phi},$$

and the Hamiltonian is

$$H = \frac{1}{2ma^2}\left(\frac{p_\xi^2 + p_\eta^2}{\sinh^2\xi + \sin^2\eta} + \frac{p_\phi^2}{\cosh^2\xi\cos^2\eta}\right) + U(\xi, \eta, \phi).$$

(B.10)

Appendix C

Laplace Equation

The Laplace equation in spherical coordinates (r, θ, ϕ) is

$$\nabla^2 \Phi = \frac{1}{r^2} \frac{\partial}{\partial r} \left(r^2 \frac{\partial \Phi}{\partial r} \right) + \frac{1}{r^2 \sin \theta} \frac{\partial}{\partial \theta} \left(\sin \theta \frac{\partial \Phi}{\partial \theta} \right) + \frac{1}{r^2 \sin^2 \theta} \frac{\partial^2 \Phi}{\partial \phi^2} = 0.$$

$$(C.1)$$

Its simplest solution is the spherically symmetric solution

$$\Phi = \frac{K}{r},$$

where K is a constant. Care must be taken, however, with the point $r = 0$. For this purpose, we can resort to Gauss' theorem to transform a volume integral to a surface integral:

$$\int dV \, \nabla^2 \Phi = \int dS \, \mathbf{n} \cdot \nabla \Phi,$$

where $\mathbf{n}$ is the unit normal to the given surface. Choosing $\Phi = 1/r$ and integrating over the surface of a sphere of radius R centered on $r = 0$, we obtain

$$\int dV \, \nabla^2 (1/r) = 4\pi R^2 \int d\Omega \left[\frac{d}{dr} (1/r) \right]_{r=R} = -4\pi.$$

Thus, we can deduce that, in general,

$$\nabla^2 \left(\frac{1}{|\mathbf{r} - \mathbf{r}'|} \right) = -4\pi \delta(\mathbf{r} - \mathbf{r}'),$$

$$(C.2)$$

introducing the Dirac delta function δ. The meaning of this last formula is that a point mass, represented by a Dirac delta, produces a potential r^{-1}.

Now, quite generally, we can expand the potential in terms of *spherical harmonics* $Y_l^m(\theta, \phi)$:

$$\Phi(\mathbf{x}) = \sum_{l=0}^{\infty} \sum_{m=-l}^{l} \frac{4\pi}{2l+1} p_{lm} \frac{Y_l^m(\theta, \phi)}{r^{l+1}}, \qquad (C.3)$$

where p_{lm} are constants to be determined for each particular mass distribution.

The complete formula is not very illuminating, so we restrict to the first spherical harmonics the $l = 0$ and $l = 1$ terms only:

$$Y_0^0(\theta, \varphi) = \frac{1}{2}\sqrt{\frac{1}{\pi}},$$

$$Y_1^{-1}(\theta, \varphi) = \frac{1}{2}\sqrt{\frac{3}{2\pi}} \sin\theta\, e^{-i\varphi},$$

$$Y_1^0(\theta, \varphi) = \frac{1}{2}\sqrt{\frac{3}{\pi}} \cos\theta,$$

$$Y_1^1(\theta, \varphi) = -\frac{1}{2}\sqrt{\frac{3}{2\pi}} \sin\theta\, e^{i\varphi}.$$

The distortion of a spherical symmetry distribution of matter will produce, at large distance r, additional terms proportional to r^{-2}, then r^{-3}, and so on.

Selected Bibliography

At an introductory level:

H. C. Corben and P. Stehle, *Classical Mechanics*, 2nd Edition (Dover, 1994).

G. R. Fowles and G. L. Cassiday, *Analytical Mechanics* (Brooks Cole, 1998).

P. Hamill, *A Student's Guide to Lagrangians and Hamiltonians* (Cambridge University Press, 2013).

D. Morin, *Introduction to Classical Mechanics: With Problems and Solutions* (Cambridge University Press, 2008).

K. R. Symon, *Mechanics*, 3rd edition (Pearson, 2017).

At an intermediate level:

M. G. Calkin, *Lagrangian and Hamiltonian Mechanics: Solutions to the Exercises* (World Scientific, 1999).

H. Goldstein, C. Poole, and J. Safko, *Classical Mechanics* (Pearson, 2001).

P. Hamill, *Intermediate Dynamics* (Cambridge University Press, 2022).

T. Kibble and F. H. Berkshire, *Classical Mechanics*, 5th Edition (Imperial College Press, 2004).

L. D. Landau and E. M. Lifshitz, *Classical Mechanics*: Volume 1: Course of Theoretical Physics (Butterworth-Heinemann, 1976).

I. Merches and D. Radu, *Analytical Mechanics: Solutions to Problems in Classical Physics* (CRC Press, 2014).

At an advanced level:

V. I. Arnold, *Mathematical Methods of Classical Mechanics* (Springer, 1997).

R. B. Bhat and R. V Dukkipati, *Advanced Dynamics* (Alpha Science International, 2001).

S. Chandrasekhar, *Ellipsoidal Figures of Equilibrium* (Dover, 1987).

M. R. Flannery, The enigma of nonholonomic constraints, *American Journal of Physics* **73**, 265 (2005).

T. M. Helliwell and V. V. Sahakian, *Modern Classical Mechanics* (Cambridge University Press, 2020).

J. V. José and E. J. Saletan, *Classical Dynamics: A Contemporary Approach* (Cambridge University Press, 1998).

L. D. Landau and E. M. Lifshitz, *The Classical Theory of Fields*, §39 (Pergamon Press, 1971).

V. Szebehely, *Theory of Orbits* (Academic Press, 1967).

Index

Printed in Great Britain
by Amazon